INDEPENDENT LEARNING PROJECT FOR ADVANCED CHEMISTRY

ILPAC
second edition

1

STARTER

THE MOLE
ATOMIC STRUCTURE

REVISED BY ANN LAINCHBURY JOHN STEPHENS ALEC THOMPSON

JOHN MURRAY

063578

■ ACKNOWLEDGEMENTS

We are grateful to CLEAPSS/ASE Laboratory Standards Committee for ensuring that the text meets with current safety recommendations.

Thanks are due to the following examination boards for permission to reproduce questions from past A-level papers: Joint Matriculation Board: Teacher-marked Exercise, p. 94 (1977). University of Cambridge Local Examinations Syndicate: Exercise 46, p. 55 (1977); End-of-unit test 10, p. 98 (1974). University of London Examinations and Assessments Council: Exercise 24, p. 24 (N 1977); Exercise 35, p. 43 (L 1980); Part A test 7, p. 28 (L 1978); Exercise 40, p. 50 (1976); Part A test 1, p. 63 (N 1980); 2, p. 63 (L 1977); 3, p. 63 (L 1982); 4, p. 63 (L 1978); 5, p. 63 (L 1987); 6, p. 64 (L 1987); 8, p. 64 (L 1980); 9, p. 64 (L 1981); 10, p. 65 (L 1992); End-of-unit test 1, p. 97 (L 1982); 2, p. 97 (L 1982); 3, p. 97 (L 1982); 4, p. 97 (L 1992); 5, p.97 (L 1989); 6, p. 97 (L 1988); 7, p. 98 (N 1978); 8, p. 98 (L 1976); 11, p. 98 (L 1973); 12, p. 98 (L 1991); 13, p. 98 (L 1981); 15, p. 101 (N 1979). University of Oxford Delegacy of Local Examinations: End-of-unit test 9, p. 98 (1979); Teacher-marked Exercise, p. 104 (1979/1980). (The examination boards accept no responsibility whatsoever for the accuracy or method of working in the answers given.)

Photographs reproduced by kind permission of: AERE Technology (p. 46 top, p. 62, p. 96); Alan Mackay, Birkbeck College (p. 71). All other photographs by the Last Resort Picture Library. The assistance provided by the staff and students of Roding Valley High School, Loughton, Essex and Tuxford School, Tuxford, Newark, Nottinghamshire for the photographs of the experiments is gratefully acknowledged.

Original material produced by the Independent Learning Project for Advanced Chemistry sponsored by the Inner London Education Authority

First edition published 1983
by John Murray (Publishers) Ltd
50 Albemarle Street
London W1X 4BD

Second edition 1995

British Library Cataloguing in Publication Data
A catalogue record for this book is available from the British Library

ISBN 0-7195-5331-8

Design and layouts by John Townson/Creation
Illustrations by Barking Dog Art

Produced by Gray Publishing
Typeset in 10/12 pt Times and Helvetica

Printed in Great Britain by St Edmundsbury Press Ltd, Bury St Edmunds

CONTENTS

■ ATOMIC STRUCTURE

INTRODUCTION TO ILPAC

These notes are intended primarily for students starting an A-level chemistry course which makes extensive use of the ILPAC materials. However, we hope you will find them helpful even if you are using perhaps only one ILPAC volume, and at any time.

You are about to spend up to two years studying A-level chemistry – so please spend a few minutes reading these notes before you begin. This is important and could save you time and effort later.

Firstly, we shall consider ways of studying effectively; secondly, we shall see how ILPAC can help.

■ How should I study?

You may never have asked yourself this question. Your teacher may have guided you so carefully that you have simply had to follow instructions – to copy notes from the blackboard, perhaps, and then to learn them and copy them out again for a test! This can be quite a good way of learning facts, but it doesn't really help you to solve problems. It protects you from thinking and taking decisions – the teacher has done that for you.

As you move towards more advanced studies, however, you must take more responsibility for your own learning – the ability to find things out for yourself is really one of the most valuable skills you can develop and, despite the electronic revolution, your most useful aids are still books.

■ How to use a textbook

Books differ in style and content and you are unlikely to find all you need for A-level chemistry in a single volume. Don't be put off if you still don't understand the topic you looked up after reading about it in one book – try another one. If you are still in difficulties, then you should go to your teacher, but you'll be surprised how quickly you realise the strengths and weaknesses of the books available to you.

'How should I read a book? Surely that's obvious – start at the beginning and keep going!' Yes, of course, if you are reading a novel. But a textbook is different. It is a mine of information, but it tells you more than you need to know to solve a particular problem. The art of using a textbook is to be selective. Look through the book to see how it breaks the subject down into chapters, sections and sub-sections. Make good use of the index, and do not be afraid to start reading in the middle of a chapter. To use an index sensibly, of course, you will need to look up significant words – 'keywords' – and, as we shall see, ILPAC can help you to do this.

So, let us suppose that you have found the right section of the textbook. What next? Well, read it and make a few notes. But is that advice as simple as it sounds? There are different ways of reading, and there are different ways of making notes. Let's look at this more closely.

■ Styles of reading

It is sometimes useful to divide methods of reading into three styles: scanning, skimming and intensive reading.

Scanning simply means running the eye rapidly down a page to search for particular words or phrases. To see how quickly you can scan a page, look up a word in the index of your textbook, say 'electron'. Turn to the first reference and look down the page so rapidly that the words are just a blur. Then slow down and look at the page again. Keep doing this, more slowly this time, until you can pick out the word you are looking for.

Skimming is slower than scanning and involves reading a passage to get an idea of its contents. Having skimmed through it, you should know whether or not the passage would repay closer study. If you cannot find what you want in one book by skimming, try another book.

Intensive reading means reading every word and studying the passage, sentence by sentence, until you have gained all the relevant information it contains.

Do remember that reading, at whatever depth, must be an active process. Be clear about what it is that you are looking for (ILPAC objectives are useful here – see below) and read for a purpose. It is quite possible to sit with glazed eyes at an open book and learn nothing!

■ Styles of note-taking

Your notes are for your benefit and so long as they are accurate and understandable by you, then they will serve their purpose. Two general points are worth making:

1. The better you have understood the material, the briefer will be your notes. They will then act as 'triggers' for your memory.
2. You should never copy out sections of text (except, perhaps, definitions and laws). Copied-out notes, neatly underlined, look reassuring but may be simply undigested material that you have not really thought about. There are at least two distinct styles of note-taking and these can be labelled 'linear' and 'patterned'.

Linear notes are ordered sequences of information, with headings and sub-headings.
Patterned notes are made by grouping words or phrases round a central idea.

To illustrate the differences between these two styles, some notes made on what has been written so far in this Introduction are shown opposite.

Whether you think these examples are particularly good notes does not really matter – that would be the concern of the students who wrote them. But do stop and ask yourself how you would have tackled the same job. Bear in mind that linear notes tend to be rather cut-and-dried (which may be appropriate) and that patterned notes are open-ended. You can always add to them and they encourage you to find connections between ideas that might not otherwise have occurred to you. In the end, however, you must develop whatever style suits you best – perhaps a combination of linear and patterned, depending upon the subject matter.

■ A reading strategy: SQR^3

Let us return to our first question – 'How should I study?' Research on how people learn shows that effective reading can be divided into stages. Here are five things you should do:

1. Survey the material you are going to read to get an overall view (e.g. scan the index and skim the more promising references).
2. Question yourself: 'Why am I doing this reading? What am I trying to find out?'
3. Read intensively the passages that you have chosen.
4. Recall: try to remember the main points from the passage you have just read. This may be an effort, but it is an important step in learning. Now is the time to make notes.
5. Review: check your notes against the passage to make sure that nothing important has been missed, and then look through your notes from time to time during the next day or two. Students who take two or three minutes to review notes within 24 hours of making them retain more of what they learn.

This reading strategy has been called, for short, SQR^3 (and sometimes SQ3R).

ILPAC Intro – Hints on study generally + ILPAC specifically

A. How to Study.

1. Copied notes not much good. Discourages thinking + Independence

2. Textbooks.
a) Look at Overall Structure
b) Use index – Keywords.
c) Scan – quick look to locate Keywords.
d) Skim – identify useful passages.
e) Intensive reading – thorough job.
f) Active reading. Read for a purpose.

3. Notes
a) Brief 'Triggers'
b) Don't copy Chunks of text (except def's, Laws ?)
c) Linear notes – like these!
d) Patterned notes – web of linked ideas radiating from central theme.

4. . . . .
      . . . .

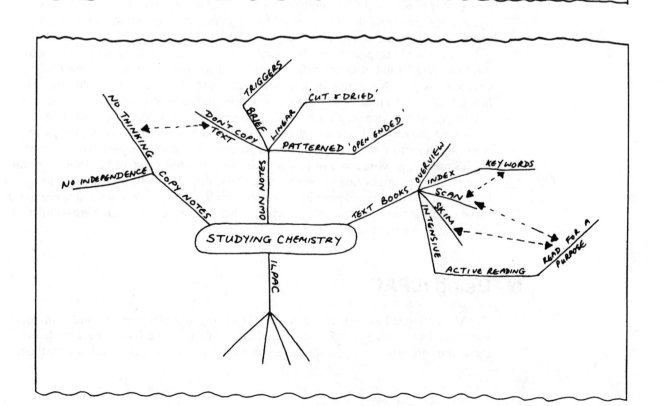

■ Time allocation for study

When to study　You will benefit more from doing an hour or two each night than by trying to catch up at weekends or in holidays. Too much study in a single day only results in inefficient learning. Try to establish your own routine, setting aside a couple of hours each night, or at least on the nights when you've had chemistry that day. Don't forget your other subjects either!

Making study sessions effective　Researchers have shown that we concentrate best for periods of 20–40 minutes without a break. After this time our attention wanders and studying efficiency falls off rapidly. So, give yourself a break every half hour or so – it may just be enough to get up and walk across the room or to have a chat with someone or look out of the window. Try to spend between one and three hours on a study session. If you find it difficult to get started, set yourself an easy task first, such as a short exercise. Getting this right will encourage you to carry on with the next task.

■ Resource-based learning

Books are essential, but are not the only sources of information. You can find out about chemistry in many ways – by watching films and television, by using computer programs, by making models, by visiting factories and laboratories and, of course, by doing experiments. These sources of information can be called resources. There is a further resource which must be added, perhaps the most important of all, the teacher. The contrast between resource-based learning and more traditional methods is conveniently illustrated by imagining two teachers at work.

The first, Mr A, is a traditionalist. He stands at the front of the class, explains the subject, gives full notes, asks questions and, once a week, supervises a practical lesson. Homework is set and marked but Mr A has such a lot of information to convey that he does not have much time to deal with individual difficulties. Because virtually all information comes through the teacher, the class moves forward together at the same steady pace. A few of the pupils find the pace too rapid and are having difficulties, but they prefer to sit quietly – it's embarrassing to hold up the rest by constantly asking questions. Others find the pace slow and are somewhat bored. Mr A's examination results are good, and all agree that he is an effective teacher.

Ms B is equally respected, and her results are also good but her approach is quite different. She is fond of saying 'Why should I tell you when you can find out for yourself?' At first, her pupils are a little disconcerted – but they soon realise that Ms B has not abandoned them. She has prepared what she calls 'Study Guides' – notes on each topic, with advice on what to read, what experiments to do, what difficulties to look out for, and so on. And, because she does not spend a great deal of time in lecturing the class, she can afford to deal with individual problems and to take part in discussions. Ms B's pupils can work more or less at their own pace, but she keeps a close watch on each person's progress, and no one is allowed to fall seriously behind. Ms B, who believes in resource-based learning, regards herself as a sort of manager; it is her job to make sure that the right resources (including her knowledge and skills) are available to the pupils at the right time.

■ Using ILPAC

ILPAC is designed to assist resource-based learning, sometimes called 'individualised learning'. The course was originally based on twenty units, each in its own book, but these units are now arranged in twelve volumes. These are not conventional textbooks, but study guides. The first three volumes form an essential starting block, because they contain material that you will need to use throughout the rest of the course, but various routes are possible thereafter. Your teacher will be able to advise you or give you a copy of suggested routes. However, some schools, and some individual students, select just some ILPAC units and integrate their use into a more conventional course of study.

Before you start working on your first unit, we suggest that you look quickly through the whole of it while reading the following notes on the main features you will find in it. This will give you an overview of the structure of a unit. You can then return to the notes later on when you reach a particular feature.

Symbols or headings in the margin will help you to find examples of each activity.

1. Pre-knowledge and pre-test

At the beginning of every unit we list, under the heading **Pre-knowledge**, some abilities which we assume you will have and which you will need to use later in the unit. Read the list and revise any topics if you think it is necessary or, if you think you have not covered a topic at all, consult your teacher. Then do the **Pre-test**, either on your own or, if your teacher prefers, in class. From the results, your teacher can tell whether you need to do any further revision before you begin the unit.

2. Parts

Most units are divided into two parts. Part A usually provides an introduction to the topic, while Part B takes you up to A-level standard. In some units, however, the parts simply divide the work into two subject areas. At the end of a unit you may find an Appendix and suggestions for further study.

3. Objectives and keywords

Objectives are statements, listed at the beginning of each section of study, which say what you should be able to do when you have finished that section. They are also a guide to important points to look for in your reading and contain emphasised 'keywords' to help you use the index of a textbook. You may also find keywords useful as a framework for making notes.

There may be some words or phrases in the objectives that are unfamiliar to you. Don't worry about this; at the end of the section you should understand them.

Your teacher should be able to give you a copy of all the objectives for a particular unit collected together in a checklist. For convenience we have condensed some of the objectives but we list them in the order in which they appear in the unit so that you can easily check your notes and use them to make summaries. Don't forget that some of the objectives will not be necessary for your particular syllabus; your teacher will advise you on this.

4. Reading

You will not find all the information you need in an ILPAC volume – we encourage you to study many topics by reading about them in textbooks and often give some guidance on points to look for and pitfalls to avoid. You should use the preceding objectives, especially the keywords, to help you find suitable passages to give purpose to your reading and to help you make notes. Here are some suggestions to help you in your reading:

1. Give yourself enough room to work – somewhere you can spread out your books and paper.
2. Go through the objectives listed above the reading task, noting the keywords. There may be some additional keywords in the reading task itself. Look up these keywords in the index of your textbook(s) and note the page numbers. If you cannot find what you want at first, try some alternative keywords – for instance, you might find 'atomic radius' under 'atom', 'radius' or 'size' or, in some indexes, under all three!

3. Turn to the page references for each objective and scan* each page in turn, looking for the keywords. In this way, identify sections that contain relevant information.
4. Skim* each of the sections you have identified, bearing in mind what you want to find out. You know this from the objectives, and also by looking at the exercises which come directly after the reading.
5. Read the passages intensively.*
6. Do the exercise(s) which follow the reading. These are designed to test your understanding of what you have just read, so you may find that you need to re-read the passage. If you still can't find what you want, you may have missed something in the index to refer you to another passage. You may even have to try another textbook!
7. Having done the exercises, look back at the objectives. Do they include anything not covered by the exercises? If so, make a note of the missing items and if you are still not happy about them when you have gone a little further, try again to find what you need in your textbook.

5. Exercises

There are numerous exercises throughout the course to help you check your progress and to give you practice in applying what you have just learned. One of the main features of ILPAC is the provision of detailed answers to all these exercises at the end of each volume. Some of the exercises (and some of the questions in the tests) are similar to questions you might encounter in an A-level examination, and the detailed answers will show you what an A-level examiner might expect to see in your answer script. These questions are identified by symbols in the margin.

Where a question is taken from a past examination paper, the examination board and the year are identified in the acknowledgements section at the beginning of the unit.

6. Worked Examples

Throughout the course, we explain calculations by means of Worked Examples. Reading carefully through a Worked Example should enable you to do the exercise(s) which follow it, although you may have to look again. If that fails, look at the method in the answer to the exercise, and then have another try. If this does not help, ask your teacher.

Don't be casual about calculations – write out every step of the solution so that it would make sense to a fellow student (and to you when you revise!) and be sure to include units. In an examination, a clearly set out method will not only help you to solve the problem correctly but will also gain you most of the marks if a simple identifiable slip leads you to a wrong answer.

Significant figures are important, and you will normally be expected to round off your answers to three significant figures, unless otherwise stated. You should look at Appendix 2 to The Mole unit of Volume 1 if you need help in understanding how to handle significant figures. A-level examiners have become increasingly strict on this and you will almost certainly be penalised if you write down your complete calculator display as an answer with no attempt to estimate significant figures correctly.

7. Teacher-marked Exercises

Teacher-marked Exercises are designed to give you practice in essay-type questions and to help your teacher to monitor your progress. Before you start one, look back at your notes on the topic to make sure you are clear about the main points, then read the question again, carefully, to make sure you answer **that** question and not a similar one with a rather different emphasis. You should try to make your answer 'fit the question' and avoid the temptation to just churn out everything you can remember about the topic, in random order! With this in mind, and with notes and textbooks closed, make a

---

*'Scanning', 'skimming' and 'intensive reading' were explained earlier in this Introduction. Look back at this if you are not sure what we mean by these terms.

short plan of your answer. Spend about half an hour writing and then hand your full answer, together with your plan, to your teacher for marking. We do not provide a specimen answer because there is nearly always more than one acceptable way to tackle the question.

8. Revealing Exercises

Also included in some of the units are Revealing Exercises, which lead you step by step, in a logical sequence of short questions and answers, through some more difficult or lengthy concepts. To start this type of exercise you cover up, with a blank sheet of paper, all but the first question. Think about an answer, and preferably write it down, before moving your blank paper down the page to reveal the given answer, and the next question. Then repeat the procedure to the end.

9. Experiments

Experiments are integrated into the course and have a variety of functions in the ILPAC scheme: some are designed to help you develop essential practical skills, while others illustrate theoretical points. There are also opportunities for you to plan your own experimental work – valuable for all students and essential for those being tested for examination purpose by practical assessments.

Ideally you should do each experiment at the time you reach it in the text, but you may have to plan ahead in order to make best use of limited laboratory time, or to ensure that the necessary equipment is made available for you.

Make sure that you have time to do the experiment and that your teacher knows that you are about to do it. You should not do practical work if your teacher is not present at the time. Also make sure that you understand the purpose of the experiment; this is stated in the Aim. The Introduction gives information needed for the experiment. Pay attention to any **hazard warnings** – these advise you on the dangers of handling certain chemicals. If you are told to wear safety spectacles or use a fume cupboard, then you **must** do so. Follow instructions carefully, making sure that you use the correct substances in the stated quantities. If laboratory time is scarce, complete the experiment before doing calculations – then you can write up the experiment at home.

Most A-level examinations include a practical test or a practical assessment by the teacher, and a written record of your work will help you achieve a suitable standard. We now give detailed suggestions for writing up experiments carefully after completing them, using most of the headings we use in the unit.

Title and aim These will be the same as in the unit.

Procedure Our instructions have to be very detailed: your account should be much briefer, more like our introduction but with enough detail added to remind you of the method.

Results tables These are designed to help you record data in a form which you can use easily. Get used to recording results clearly as you work – scribbled figures on scraps of paper can be confusing even if you don't lose them! Your teacher may be able to give you duplicated blank tables.

Calculations You must include enough explanation to enable you to follow the calculations when you revise. A couple of lines of scribbled figures with no indication of method is quite useless. Our specimen calculations are a good guide.

Questions We include these to help you understand the method and its limitations. Your answers should therefore be useful in revision. Either copy out the questions or write your answer in such a way that the question is also included. Avoid answers beginning 'Because . . . ' – they are likely to be grammatically incorrect and are not at all helpful in revision unless the question is stated.

Comment Finish your account with a comment on the accuracy of your results and, if they are poor, some indication of the probable reasons.

10. Video programmes

A series of video-cassettes (VHS) has been made to accompany the units. You should find them very helpful but, if they are not available, you can still follow ILPAC without them. Your teacher has a list of the videos.

Before you watch a programme, find out how long it lasts and whether there is time to see it more than once and/or to stop it at convenient points for note-taking and discussion. Have a pen and paper ready because you are often asked to record data during a programme.

If you have time, it is a good idea to watch a programme straight through first, and then make notes on the points you want to remember during a second showing.

11. Computer programs

There are many educational computer programs, available commercially or through teachers' centres, which may be relevant to some topics in your course, particularly the more mathematical ones. They introduce some variety to your activities and may help you to understand some ideas better. However, as with the videos, you can still follow ILPAC without them.

We no longer recommend specific programs because new and updated programs are being released all the time. Also, some of those we might recommend were written for a particular computer and might not work on the machines available to you. Your teacher should have a list of resources and be able to help you choose suitable programs.

12. Model-making

Making three-dimensional models of molecules and giant structures can be very helpful in interpreting two-dimensional diagrams in books. For some people, it is the **only** way to understand fully how shapes of molecules and bond angles affect the course of chemical reactions. This can be most important in your study of organic chemistry.

13. Data book

You will refer frequently to your data book throughout this course so you must learn how to use it effectively.

For example, you may be asked to use your data book to calculate molar masses. Turn to the index and find the page reference(s) for molar mass or relative atomic mass. If there is more than one reference, look at them all and see which is most convenient for your purpose. A table which gives very precise values may be confusing if you only need approximate values. Is it easier to have the elements listed alphabetically or by atomic number?

Always look carefully at the headings of columns in tables of data, and read any accompanying notes to make sure that the data are really what you want and that you quote the correct units.

14. Tests (End-of-part and End-of-unit)

After your revision, based on the checklist of objectives (see above), attempt the test at the end of each part. The test is designed to show **you** what you should have learned and to help your teacher to monitor your progress. Where appropriate, A-level questions are included.

If your teacher agrees, you could do the test at home but resist the temptation to study the questions, and observe the rules – only you will lose out if you cheat!

15. End-of-unit summary

It is a good idea to summarise the contents of each unit on a **single sheet** of paper. Look again at the section on note-taking at the beginning of this Introduction to ILPAC.

■ Symbols used in ILPAC

 Computer program

 A- level question

 Discussion

 A-level part question

 Experiment

 A-level question; Special Paper

 Model-making

 A-level supplementary question

 Reading

 Revealing Exercise

 Video programme

■ International hazard symbols

 Corrosive

 Oxidising

 Explosive

 Radioactive

 Harmful or irritant

 Toxic

 Highly flammable

THE MOLE

INTRODUCTION

In this first unit we help you to consolidate some of the ideas about the mole which you have already met in your pre-A-level course.

In Part A we begin by considering relative masses and then develop the concept of the mole as the unit amount of substance. We use the mole concept in stoichiometric calculations to determine how much material is used in a chemical reaction and how to find the empirical formula of a compound.

In Part B we extend the concept of stoichiometry to reactions in solution and show you how to apply it in a variety of titrations. There are five experiments in this unit.

There are two ILPAC video programmes designed to accompany this unit. Their use is not essential, but you should try to see them at the appropriate time if they are available.

Preparing a standard solution.

Performing a titration.

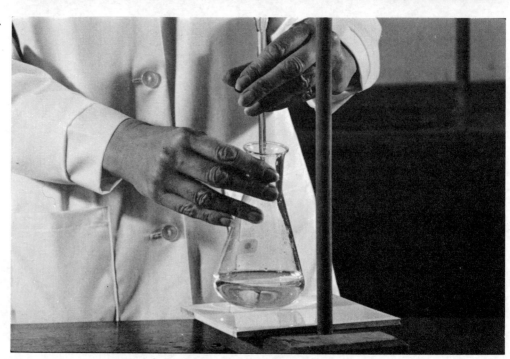

■ Pre-knowledge

See the notes in the Introduction to ILPAC. Before you start work on this unit you should be able to:
- ■ express numbers in standard form;
- ■ multiply and divide numbers expressed in standard form;
- ■ state whether a given formula refers to an atom, an ion or a molecule;
- ■ identify and name pieces of common laboratory glassware;
- ■ write the empirical formula of a compound, given its molecular formula.

■ Pre-test

See the notes in the Introduction to ILPAC. To find out whether you are ready to start Part A, try the following test, which is based on the pre-knowledge items. You should not spend more than 30 minutes on this test. Hand your answers to your teacher for marking.

1. Numbers written in the form 1.7×10^9 and 9.26×10^{-5} are said to be written in standard form.
    Express in standard form the following numbers:
    a 0.000 000 000 500,   **b** 301 000 000. (2)

2. Work out the following, without using a calculator:

    a $\dfrac{10^7}{10^2}$

    b $\dfrac{10^9}{10^{-9}}$

    c $\dfrac{1.3 \times 10^{12}}{2.6 \times 10^{23}}$

    d $\dfrac{1.0 \times 10^{-6}}{5.0 \times 10^{-6}}$ (4)

3. The mass of a hydrogen atom is 1.67×10^{-24} g, the mass of a carbon atom is 1.99×10^{-23} g, the mass of an oxygen atom is 2.66×10^{-23} g and the mass of a sodium atom is 3.82×10^{-23} g. Calculate the following ratios:

    a $\dfrac{\text{mass of a carbon atom}}{\text{mass of a hydrogen atom}}$

    b $\dfrac{\text{mass of an oxygen atom}}{\text{mass of a hydrogen atom}}$

    c $\dfrac{\text{mass of a sodium atom}}{\text{mass of a hydrogen atom}}$ (3)

4. Do the following calculation, expressing your answer in standard form:

    $$\frac{50\,000\,000 \times 0.000\,000\,000\,000\,6}{1.5}$$ (1)

5. Identify each of the following as 'an atom', 'an ion' or 'a molecule'.
    a Na   **b** F_2 **c** O^{2-}
    d O   **e** SO_4^{2-} **f** IO_3^- (6)

6. Name each of the following common pieces of laboratory equipment. Choose your answers from the following list.
   - ■ burette
   - ■ volumetric flask
   - ■ beaker
   - ■ limpette
   - ■ conical flask
   - ■ measuring cylinder
   - ■ evaporating dish
   - ■ pipette
   - ■ filter funnel

(6)

Figure 1

(a)
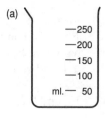

(b)
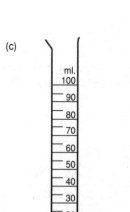

(c)

(d)

(e)

(f)
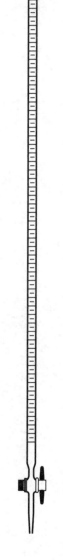

7. What is the empirical formula of
   a propene, C_3H_6,
   b hydrogen peroxide, H_2O_2,
   c ethanoic acid, CH_3CO_2H?

(3)

(Total: 25 marks)

In the early part of this unit, we want to develop the idea of relative mass of atoms. First, we clarify what we mean by 'relative mass'.

CHAPTER

1 RELATIVE MASS

The mass of any object expressed in any unit is measured relative to some standard. For example, the universal standard of mass is a block of platinum–iridium alloy, called the standard kilogram, which is kept in France at Sèvres, near Paris.

If you buy five kilograms of potatoes, you have five times the mass of the standard kilogram. There are two ways of expressing this:

'The mass of the potatoes is 5 kg.'

'The relative mass of the potatoes on the kilogram scale is 5.'

In general, relative mass $= \dfrac{\text{actual mass}}{\text{mass of a suitable standard}}$

Now you can apply the idea of relative mass to atoms.

■ 1.1 Relative atomic mass

Atoms are so small that their masses expressed in grams are difficult to work with. Some examples are listed in Table 1.

Table 1

Element	Average mass of an atom/g
H	1.67355×10^{-24}
He	6.64605×10^{-24}
Li	1.15217×10^{-23}
C	1.99436×10^{-23}
O	2.65659×10^{-23}
Na	3.81730×10^{-23}
Ar	6.63310×10^{-23}
U	3.95233×10^{-22}

However, the mass of an atom expressed as relative atomic mass (RAM) is much more manageable. We measure the mass of an atom compared to the mass of a chosen standard atom.

An atom of hydrogen was the chosen standard for the first atomic mass scale because hydrogen is the lightest element. It was convenient to have all relative atomic masses greater than (or equal to) 1.

Hydrogen was abandoned as a standard for a number of reasons, one being that so few elements combine with it. A new standard, based on oxygen, was chosen.

After the adoption of the oxygen scale, scientists discovered that oxygen is a mixture of isotopes.* The composition of the mixture varies slightly and so, therefore, does the average mass of an oxygen atom which was used as a standard. It became necessary to adopt a new standard which does not vary.

The new standard is based on the mass of the most abundant isotope of carbon, carbon-12 (^{12}C).

■ 1.2 The relative atomic mass scale

EXERCISE 1

Answers on page 105

Use the values in Table 1 to calculate atomic masses relative to
a hydrogen,
b oxygen,
c carbon-12.

Enter your values into a copy of Results Table 1. Some values are included as a check. (The mass of an atom of carbon-12 = 1.99252×10^{-23} g.)

Results Table 1

Element	Relative atomic mass (RAM)		
	H scale	O scale	^{12}C scale
H	1.00000	1.00794	1.00790
He		4.00276	
Li	6.88459		
C			12.01110
O		16.0000	
Na	22.8096		
Ar		39.9496	
U			238.030

In most of your A-level work, you use relative atomic masses expressed to three significant figures, e.g. He = 4.00, O = 16.0, Ar = 39.9, U = 238. To this degree of precision, the oxygen scale and the carbon-12 scale can be regarded as the same, but you should never use the hydrogen scale because it differs so much from the others.

For more accurate work, the difference between the oxygen and carbon-12 scales is important and in 1961, IUPAC (the International Union of Pure and Applied Chemistry) adopted the carbon-12 scale as standard. These values are quoted in all publications since that date.

You will learn more about the methods of measuring relative atomic mass in the next unit. In this unit you use relative atomic mass in calculations involving amounts of substance.

---

*Isotopes are atoms of an element which have almost identical properties except that their masses differ due to having different numbers of neutrons (see the next unit: Atomic Structure).

2 AMOUNT

You have already learned to give special scientific meanings to familiar everyday words like 'element' and 'compound'. Now you look more closely at the familiar word 'amount'.

OBJECTIVE When you have finished this chapter you should be able to:
■ calculate the **amount** of identical objects, given the mass of each object and the mass per unit amount of objects.

'Amount' is another physical quantity like mass, volume, length, time, etc. It gives us an alternative, and very useful, way of expressing how much there is of a substance.

We can express how much there is of a substance as a mass (by reference to a standard mass), as a volume (by reference to a standard volume), or as an amount (by reference to a standard **counting unit**).

As with all other physical quantities, an amount is written as a number times an associated unit:

$$\text{mass} = 10.2 \text{ kg}$$
$$\text{time} = 42.1 \text{ s}$$
$$\text{temperature} = 273 \text{ K}$$
$$\text{length} = 0.7 \text{ m}$$
$$\text{volume} = 24.2 \text{ cm}^3$$
$$\text{amount} = 19 \text{ dozen}$$

■ 2.1 Calculating amount by weighing

Coins can be counted by weighing them. For example, if a cashier in a bank is given a bag containing 2p coins which is found to have a mass of 356 g, then she knows that the bag contains 50 coins. If the bag weighs 178 g, then she knows that the bag contains 25 coins, and so on. (Each 2p coin weighs 7.12 g.)

We can generalise this relationship in the following expression:

$$\text{amount of objects} = \frac{\text{mass of objects}}{\text{mass per unit amount of objects}}$$

By 'unit amount' we mean one dozen, one gross, one ream, etc. You use this idea in the next two exercises.

Throughout the course, you are expected to give the answers to numerical exercises correct to three significant figures (unless otherwise stated). You should see Appendix 2, page 41, for the use of significant figures in calculations.

EXERCISE 2
Answers on page 105

One dozen pencils weighs 45.0 g. Calculate the amount of pencils in a consignment weighing 5625 g.

EXERCISE 3
Answers on page 105

One gross (144) of paper clips weighs 82.08 g. A sample of paper clips weighs 5.13×10^6 g.
a Calculate the amount of paper clips (in units of gross) in the sample.
b How many paper clips are there in the sample?

■ 2.2 Amount of substance – the mole

As objects get smaller, the number in a unit amount gets larger; for example, we buy a pair of socks, a dozen eggs and a ream (500 sheets) of paper.

In counting atoms we also need a convenient unit, large enough to be seen and handled. Since atoms are so small, there are a great many of them in a convenient unit.

OBJECTIVES When you have finished this section you should be able to:
■ define (a) **the mole** and (b) **molar mass**;
■ quote the value of the **Avogadro constant** to three significant figures.

The counting unit for atoms, molecules and ions is the mole (symbol: mol). **The mole is defined as the amount of substance that contains as many elementary particles as there are atoms in exactly 0.012 kg (12 g) of carbon-12**. You must learn this definition.

The mass of an atom of carbon-12 is 1.99252×10^{-23} g. So the number of atoms in 12 g of carbon-12 is given by

$$\frac{12 \text{ g}}{1.99252 \times 10^{-23} \text{ g}} = 6.02252 \times 10^{23}$$

Note that in this context, 12 is taken to be an integer and it does not therefore limit the significant figures in the answer to two.

The Avogadro constant (symbol: L) relates the number of particles to the amount. It is represented as $L = 6.02252 \times 10^{23} \text{ mol}^{-1}$ or, to three significant figures,

$$L = 6.02 \times 10^{23} \text{ mol}^{-1}$$

The following examples try to convey the magnitude of the Avogadro constant.

If you were to have 6.02×10^{23} tiny grains of pollen they would cover the City of London to a depth of 1 mile.

Figure 2

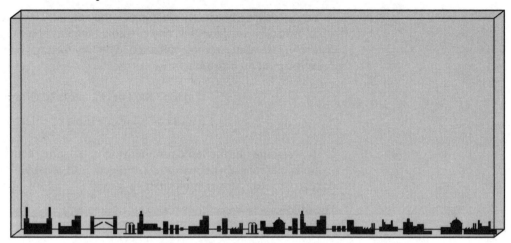

If 6.02×10^{23} marshmallows were spread over the United States of America this would yield a blanket of marshmallows more than 600 miles deep!

Computers can count about 10 million times per second. At this rate 6.02×10^{23} counts would require almost 2 billion years.

A similar example is included in the next exercise.

EXERCISE 4

Answers on page 105

A 5 cm³ spoon can hold 1.67×10^{23} molecules of water.

a How long would it take to remove them one at a time at a rate of one molecule per second?

b How many years is this?

■ 2.3 Molar mass

The mass per unit amount of substance is called its molar mass (symbol: M) and is the mass per mole of that substance. We usually use the unit: g mol⁻¹.

OBJECTIVE

When you have finished this section you should be able to:
■ calculate the **molar mass** of a substance, given its formula and a table of relative atomic masses.

The molar mass of an element is the mass per mole. It follows from the definition of the mole that the molar mass of carbon is 12.0 g mol⁻¹. Similarly, since the relative atomic mass of uranium is 238, M = 238 g mol⁻¹.

The term molar mass applies not only to elements in the atomic state but also to all chemical species – atoms, molecules, ions, etc.

For ethane, the molar mass is calculated from its formula, C_2H_6, which indicates that one molecule contains two atoms of carbon and six atoms of hydrogen. The relative atomic masses are: C = 12.0, H = 1.0. The relative mass of a molecule on the same scale is therefore given by:

$$C_2H_6$$

$$(2 \times 12.0) + (6 \times 1.0) = 30.0$$

Thus, the relative molecular mass of ethane is 30.0 and its molar mass, $M = 30.0$ g mol^{-1}. There are two important points which you must bear in mind when dealing with amounts of substances:

1. You must specify exactly what entity the amount refers to. The phrase '1 mol of chlorine', for instance, has two possible meanings because it does not specify whether it refers to atoms or molecules. To avoid confusion, you must always specify the entity, either by formula or in words:

    1.0 mol of Cl **or** one mole of chlorine atoms

    1.0 mol of Cl$_2$ **or** one mole of chlorine molecules

2. By weighing out the same number of grams as the relative atomic mass or the relative molecular mass (whether atoms, molecules or ions) you have measured out one mole, i.e. 6.02×10^{23} atoms, molecules or ions.

The following two exercises test your understanding of these concepts and give you practice in using your data book.

EXERCISE 5
Answers on page 105

Using your data book, calculate the molar masses of
a   ammonia, NH$_3$,
b   calcium bromide, CaBr$_2$,
c   phosphoric(V) acid, H$_3$PO$_4$,
d   sodium sulphate-10-water, Na$_2$SO$_4$·10H$_2$O.

EXERCISE 6
Answers on page 106

What is the mass of 1.00 mol of
a   chlorine atoms,
b   chlorine, Cl$_2$,
c   phosphorus, P,
d   phosphorus, P$_4$,
e   iodide ions, I$^-$?

■ 2.4 Amount calculations

OBJECTIVES

When you have finished this section you should be able to:
■ calculate the amount of a substance given its mass and molar mass;
■ calculate the number of particles in a given amount.

In Exercise 2 you determined the amount of pencils by using the expression:

$$\text{amount of pencils} = \frac{\text{mass}}{\text{mass per dozen}}$$

In science, the amount of substance in a given sample is similarly defined as the mass of the sample divided by the mass per mole (i.e. the molar mass):

$$\text{amount of substance} = \frac{\text{mass}}{\text{molar mass}}$$

The symbol for amount is n and, therefore, in symbols:

$$n = \frac{m}{M}$$

The following Worked Example shows you how to use this expression in mole calculations.

Reminder: the unit for amount is mole, for mass is gram, and for molar mass is grams per mole (abbreviation: $g\ mol^{-1}$).

WORKED EXAMPLE   A sample of carbon weighs 180 g. What amount of carbon is present?

Solution   Calculate the amount by substituting into the key expression:

$$n = \frac{m}{M}$$

where $m = 180$ g and $M = 12.0\ g\ mol^{-1}$.

$$\therefore n = \frac{m}{M} = \frac{180\ g}{12.0\ g\ mol^{-1}} = 15.0\ mol$$

At this point you should make sure that you are not using the formula in a mechanical way but understand what you are doing. So, here is an alternative method which relies on first principles. **You should never substitute into an expression without first understanding how it was derived or defined.**

Alternative solution   1. Write down the mass of 1.00 mol of the substance in the form of a sentence:

12.0 g is the mass of 1.00 mol of carbon.

2. Scale down to the amount of carbon in 1.00 g by dividing by 12.0 throughout:

$$\frac{12.0\ g}{12.0}\ \text{is the mass of}\ \frac{1.00\ mol}{12.0}\ \text{of carbon}$$

3. Scale up to the amount of carbon in 180 g by multiplying by 180 throughout:

$$180 \times \frac{12.0\ g}{12.0}\ \text{is the mass of}\ 180 \times \frac{1.00\ mol}{12.0}\ \text{of carbon}$$

i.e. 180 g is the mass of 15.0 mol of carbon
∴ the amount of carbon in 180 g is 15.0 mol.

Now attempt the following exercises. (We use the method of substituting into the expression in our answers, largely because it takes up less space. You can try the 'sentence method' if you get stuck.)

EXERCISE 7   Calculate the amount in each of the following:
Answers on page 106   **a**   30.0 g of oxygen molecules, O_2,
  b   31.0 g of phosphorus molecules, P_4,
  c   50.0 g of calcium carbonate, $CaCO_3$.

You must also be prepared for questions which ask you to calculate the mass of substance in a given amount. To do this in the following exercises, use the expression:

$$n = \frac{m}{M}\ \text{in the form}\ m = nM$$

EXERCISE 8
Answers on page 106

Calculate the mass of each of the following:
a 1.00 mol of hydrogen, H_2,
b 0.500 mol of sodium chloride, NaCl,
c 0.250 mol of carbon dioxide, CO_2.

EXERCISE 9
Answers on page 106

A sample of ammonia, NH_3, weighs 1.00 g.
a What amount of ammonia is contained in this sample?
b What mass of sulphur dioxide, SO_2, contains the same number of molecules as are in 1.00 g of ammonia?

We now consider another type of amount calculation.

■ 2.5 Calculating the number of particles in a given amount

Sometimes you are required to calculate the number of particles in a given amount of substance. This is easy because you know the number of particles in 1.00 mol (6.02×10^{23}). Use the expression:

$$N = nL$$

where N = the number of particles, n = the amount, L = the Avogadro constant.

EXERCISE 10
Answers on page 107

Calculate the number of atoms in:
a 18.0 g of carbon, C,
b 18.0 g of copper, Cu,
c 7.20 g of sulphur, S_8.

EXERCISE 11
Answers on page 107

Calculate the number of molecules in:
a 1.00 g of ammonia, NH_3,
b 3.28 g of sulphur dioxide, SO_2,
c 7.20 g of sulphur, S_8.

EXERCISE 12
Answers on page 108

Calculate the number of ions present in:
a 0.500 mol of sodium chloride, NaCl (Na^+, Cl^-),
b 14.6 g of sodium chloride, NaCl,
c 18.5 g of calcium chloride, $CaCl_2$.

The Avogadro constant is an important quantity, and at least 20 different methods have been devised to measure or calculate it. The next experiment illustrates a simple method which is capable of giving an approximate value.

EXPERIMENT 1   Determining the Avogadro constant

OBJECTIVE

When you have finished this experiment you should be able to:
■ calculate the Avogadro constant from data obtained in the monomolecular layer experiment.

Aim   The purpose of this experiment is to estimate the value of the Avogadro constant and to compare this estimate with the accepted value.

Introduction   When a solution of oleic acid (more correctly called *cis*-octadec-9-enoic acid), $C_{17}H_{33}CO_2H$, in pentane is dropped onto water, the pentane evaporates leaving behind a layer of oleic acid one molecule thick. For this reason, this experiment has been called 'The Monomolecular Layer Experiment'.

You use a loop of hair or thread to contain the oleic acid and to give a measure of the surface area. By making certain assumptions about the shape of the molecule and its alignment on the surface, you can get a reasonably accurate value for the Avogadro constant.

The experiment has two parts. In the first, you calibrate the pipette. This gives the volume of one drop of solution. In the second part you determine how many drops of solution are required to just fill the loop with a layer of oleic acid molecules. Then we lead you, step by step, through the calculation.

Requirements   ■ safety spectacles
■ measuring cylinder, 10 cm^3
■ teat pipette and adaptor (for small drops)
■ trough
■ human hair or cotton thread, 40–50 cm
■ scissors
■ petroleum jelly or Vaseline
■ oleic acid solution in pentane (0.05 cm^3 of oleic acid per dm^3)

HAZARD WARNING Pentane is extremely flammable and harmful by inhalation. Therefore you **must**:
■ keep the stopper on the bottle when not in use;
■ keep the liquid away from flames.

Procedure

1. Fill the teat pipette with oleic acid solution and deliver it drop by drop into the 10 cm³ measuring cylinder. Count the number of drops which must be delivered from the pipette to reach the 1 cm³ mark. Enter your value in a copy of Results Table 2.

Results Table 2

Number of drops to deliver 1 cm³ of solution	Number of drops delivered to make monomolecular layer	Diameter of monomolecular layer/cm

2. Tie the hair or cotton thread in a loop. Use a reef-knot (Fig. 3), rather than an overhand knot, so that the loop will make a flat circle. Cut the ends as close as to the knot as possible. Hair is preferred because it does not need greasing but if you are using thread, thoroughly but lightly grease it with petroleum jelly. It is most important that no part of the thread escapes greasing. Run the knotted thread through your fingers several times before wiping off the excess.

Figure 3

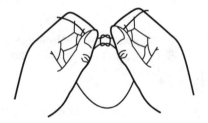

3. Fill the trough with water and float the loop on it, making sure that the entire circumference is in contact with the surface. Look very carefully for 'bridges' or submerged loops and move them into the surface with a clean glass rod or a pencil point.

4. Using the same pipette, add the oleic acid solution dropwise to the middle of the loop until it is filled. At first you will probably see the loop expand to a circle and then retract again.
   Before the loop is filled, it 'gives' when you push it gently from the outside with a pencil (Fig. 4).
   When the loop is filled, it will slide across the surface, only denting very slightly when pushed gently with the pencil (Fig. 5).

Figure 4

Figure 5

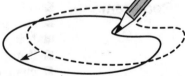

Count the number of drops required to fill the loop and record this in a copy of Results Table 2.

5. Measure the diameter of the loop and complete Results Table 2.
6. If you have time, repeat the whole procedure. However, you must use a fresh hair or thread, and wash out the trough thoroughly to obtain a clean surface.

Calculation

1. Calculate the volume of 1 drop delivered from the teat pipette using the value in column one of Results Table 2.

$$\text{Volume of 1 drop} = \underline{\quad} \text{ cm}^3$$

2. Calculate the volume of oleic acid in 1 drop of solution delivered from the teat pipette.
Remember that 1000 cm^3 of this solution contains 0.05 cm^3 of oleic acid.

$$\text{Volume of oleic acid in 1 drop} = \underline{\quad} \text{ cm}^3$$

3. Calculate the volume of oleic acid delivered to make the monomolecular layer; i.e. the volume of oleic acid in 1 drop × the number of drops required.

$$\text{Volume of oleic acid in monolayer} = \underline{\quad} \text{ cm}^3$$

4. Calculate the surface area of the oleic acid layer.

$$\text{Area} = \pi d^2/4 = \underline{\quad} \text{ cm}^2$$

5. You know the volume of oleic acid (from 3) and the surface area it covers (from 4). It is a simple matter to calculate the thickness of the layer because volume = area × thickness.

$$\text{Thickness} = \underline{\quad} \text{ cm.}$$

Figure 6

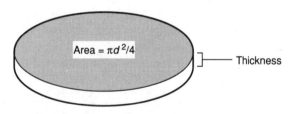

6. Calculate the volume of one molecule of oleic acid by assuming that it is a cube, with sides equal to the thickness of the layer.

$$\text{Volume of one molecule} = \underline{\quad} \text{ cm}^3$$

7. Calculate the volume of a mole of oleic acid given that its density is 0.890 g cm^{-3} and its molar mass is 282 g mol^{-1}.

$$\text{Volume per mole of oleic acid} = \underline{\quad} \text{ cm}^3 \text{ mol}^{-1}$$

8. Divide the volume per mole by the volume of one molecule to determine the Avogadro constant.

$$L = \underline{\quad} \text{ mol}^{-1}.$$

(There is a set of specimen results on page 109.)

Answers on page 109

Questions

1. Suggest some sources of error in this experiment which account for the discrepancy between the value of L that you obtained and the accepted value of $L = 6.02 \times 10^{23}$ mol^{-1}.

2. Which of the values that you used in your calculations is subject to the greatest error?

3. Pentane is not the only liquid that can be used in this experiment. Suggest four properties which a suitable substitute must have.

We now consider how we can use the mole concept to calculate how much of one substance will react with a given amount of another – this is called stoichiometry and is one of the main reasons why the mole concept is so important in the study of chemistry.

3 STOICHIOMETRY

Stoichiometry (pronounced stoy-key-om-i-tree) in its broadest sense includes all the quantitative relationships in chemical reactions. It has to do with how much of one substance will react with another. A chemical equation such as

$$N_2\,(g) + 3H_2\,(g) \rightarrow 2NH_3\,(g)$$

is a kind of chemical balance sheet; it states that one mole of nitrogen reacts with three moles of hydrogen to yield two moles of ammonia. (It does **not** tell us about the rate of the reaction or the conditions necessary to bring it about.) The numbers 1, 3 and 2 are called the stoichiometric coefficients. Such an equation is an essential starting point for many experiments and calculations; it tells us the proportions in which the substances react and in which the products are formed.

OBJECTIVE

When you have finished this chapter you should be able to:
■ do simple reacting mass calculations based on a given chemical equation, i.e. **stoichiometric** calculations.

We start with a Worked Example.

WORKED EXAMPLE

What mass of iodine will react completely with 10.0 g of aluminium?

This problem is a little more complicated than those you have done previously, because it involves several steps. Each step is very simple, but you may not immediately see where to start. Before we present a detailed solution, let us look at a way of approaching multi-step problems. Even if you find this problem easy, the approach may be useful to you in more difficult problems. We suggest that you ask yourself three questions:

1. What do I know?
In this case, the answer should be:
a the equation for the reaction;
b the mass of aluminium.

In some problems you may be given the equation; in this one, you are expected to write it down from your general chemical knowledge. In nearly every problem about a reaction, the equation provides vital information.

2. What can I get from what I know?
a From the equation, I can find the ratio of reacting amounts.
b From the mass of aluminium, I can calculate the amount, provided I look up the molar mass.

3. Can I now see how to get the final answer?
In most cases the answer will be 'Yes', but you may have to ask the second question again, now that you know more than you did at the start.
a From the amount of aluminium and the ratio of reacting amounts, I can calculate the amount of iodine.
b From the amount of iodine, I can get the mass, using the molar mass.

Instead of writing answers to these questions, you can summarise your thinking in a flow diagram.

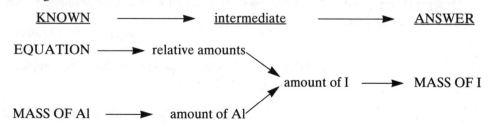

An alternative strategy is to work backwards from the answer towards the given information, or you may use a combination of both strategies, meeting up in the middle. In any case, the steps that you use will probably be the same, although the order in which you take them may be different. Now we go through each step, using the first strategy, and doing the necessary calculations.

Solution   1. Write the balanced equation for the reaction:

$$2Al\ (s) + 3I_2\ (s) \rightarrow 2AlI_3\ (s)$$

This equation tells us that 2 mol of Al reacts with 3 mol of I_2; so we write the ratio:

$$\frac{\text{amount of Al}}{\text{amount of } I_2} = \frac{2}{3}$$

2. Calculate the amount of aluminium using the expression:

$$n = \frac{m}{M}$$

$$\therefore\ n = \frac{10.0\ \text{g}}{27.0\ \text{g mol}^{-1}} = 0.370\ \text{mol}$$

3. Calculate the amount of iodine which reacts with this amount of aluminium by substituting into the expression based on the equation:

$$\frac{\text{amount of Al}}{\text{amount of } I_2} = \frac{2}{3}$$

$$\therefore\ \text{amount of } I_2 = \frac{3}{2} \times \text{amount of Al}$$

$$= \frac{3}{2} \times 0.370\ \text{mol} = 0.555\ \text{mol}$$

4. Calculate the mass of iodine from the amount using the expression:

$$n = \frac{m}{M} \quad \text{in the form} \quad m = nM$$

$$\therefore m = nM = 0.555\ \text{mol} \times 254\ \text{g mol}^{-1} = 141\ \text{g}$$

Now try some similar problems for yourself.

EXERCISE 13   **a** What mass of magnesium would react completely with 16.0 g of sulphur?
Answers on page 110

$$Mg\ (s) + S\ (s) \rightarrow MgS\ (s)$$

b What mass of oxygen would be produced by completely decomposing 4.25 g of sodium nitrate, $NaNO_3$?

$$2NaNO_3\ (s) \rightarrow 2NaNO_2\ (s) + O_2\ (g)$$

EXERCISE 14
Answers on page 110

What mass of phosphorus(V) oxide, P_2O_5, would be formed by complete oxidation of 4.00 g of phosphorus?

$$4P \text{ (s)} + 5O_2 \text{ (g)} \rightarrow 2P_2O_5 \text{ (s)}$$

EXERCISE 15
Answers on page 111

When 0.27 g of aluminium is added to excess copper(II) sulphate solution, 0.96 g of copper is precipitated. Deduce the equation for the reaction which takes place.

In the next exercise you have to decide first which one of two reactants is present in excess.

EXERCISE 16
Answers on page 112

A mixture containing 2.80 g of iron and 2.00 g of sulphur is heated together. What mass of iron(II) sulphide, FeS, is produced?

$$\text{Fe (s)} + \text{S (s)} \rightarrow \text{FeS (s)}$$

Another important application of the mole concept is in the calculation of the empirical formulae of substances.

CHAPTER 4

CALCULATING EMPIRICAL FORMULAE

The empirical formula of a compound is the simplest form of the ratio of the atoms of different elements in it. The molecular formula tells the actual number of each kind of atom in a molecule of the substance. For example, the molecular formula of phosphorus(V) oxide is P_4O_{10}, whereas its empirical formula is P_2O_5.

OBJECTIVE

When you have finished this chapter you should be able to:
■ calculate the **empirical formula** of a compound, given either
  a the masses of constituents in a sample, or
  b the composition in terms of the mass percentages of the constituents.

■ 4.1 Calculating the empirical formula from the masses of constituents

To determine the empirical formula of a compound, we must first calculate the amount of each substance present in a sample and then calculate the simplest whole-number ratio of the amounts.

It is convenient to set the results out in tabular form and we suggest that you use this method. However, in the following Worked Example, we will go through the procedure step by step, establishing the table as we go.

WORKED EXAMPLE

An 18.3 g sample of a hydrated compound contained 4.0 g of calcium, 7.1 g of chlorine and 7.2 g of water only. Calculate its empirical formula.

Solution

1. List the mass of each component and its molar mass. Although water is a molecule, in the calculation we treat it in the same way as we do atoms.

	Ca	Cl	H_2O
Mass/g	4.0	7.1	7.2
Molar mass/g mol^{-1}	40.0	35.5	18.0

2. From this information calculate the amount of each substance present using the expression $n = m/M$.

	Ca	Cl	H_2O
Amount/mol	$\dfrac{4.0}{40.0} = 0.10$	$\dfrac{7.1}{35.5} = 0.20$	$\dfrac{7.2}{18.0} = 0.40$

(For simplicity, we have omitted the units from the calculation – they cancel anyway.) This result means that in the given sample there is 0.10 mol of calcium, 0.20 mol of chlorine and 0.40 mol of water.

3. Calculate the **relative** amount of each substance by dividing each amount by the smallest amount.

	Ca	Cl	H_2O
Amount/smallest amount = relative amount	$\dfrac{0.10}{0.10} = 1.0$	$\dfrac{0.20}{0.10} = 2.0$	$\dfrac{0.40}{0.10} = 4.0$

The relative amounts are in the simple ratio 1:2:4.
From this result you can see that the empirical formula is $CaCl_2 \cdot 4H_2O$.
To see if you understand this procedure, try Exercise 17.

EXERCISE 17
Answer on page 112

A sample of a hydrated compound was analysed and found to contain 2.10 g of cobalt, 1.14 g of sulphur, 2.28 g of oxygen and 4.50 g of water. Calculate its empirical formula.

A modification of this type of problem is to determine the ratio of the amount of water to the amount of anhydrous compound. You have practice in this type of problem in the next exercise.

EXERCISE 18
Answer on page 113

10.00 g of hydrated barium chloride is heated until all the water is driven off. The mass of anhydrous compound is 8.53 g. Determine the value of x in $BaCl_2 \cdot xH_2O$.

You should be prepared for variations to this type of problem. The following part of an A-level question illustrates such a variation.

EXERCISE 19
Answer on page 113

When 585 mg of the salt $UO(C_2O_4) \cdot 6H_2O$ was left in a vacuum desiccator for 48 hours, the mass changed to 535 mg. What formula would you predict for the resulting substance?

Now look at another way of calculating empirical formula.

■ 4.2 Calculating empirical formula from percentage composition by mass

The result of the analysis of a compound may also be given in terms of the percentage composition by mass. Study the following Worked Example which deals with this type of problem.

WORKED EXAMPLE

An organic compound was analysed and was found to have the following percentage composition by mass: 48.8% carbon, 13.5% hydrogen and 37.7% nitrogen. Calculate the empirical formula of the compound.

Solution

If we consider a sample with mass 100.0 g, we can write immediately the mass of each substance: 48.8 g of carbon, 13.5 g of hydrogen and 37.7 g of nitrogen. Then we set up a table as before. The instructions between each step are omitted this time, but you should check our calculations.

	C	H	N
Mass/g	48.8	13.5	37.7
Molar mass/g mol^{-1}	12.0	1.00	14.0
Amount/mol	4.07	13.5	2.69
$\dfrac{\text{Amount}}{\text{Smallest amount}}$	$\dfrac{4.07}{2.69} = 1.51$	$\dfrac{13.5}{2.69} = 5.02$	$\dfrac{2.69}{2.69} = 1.00$
Simplest ratio of relative amounts	3	10	2

Empirical formula = $C_3H_{10}N_2$

In the preceding exercises you 'rounded off' values close to whole numbers in order to get a simple ratio. This is justified because small differences from whole numbers are probably due to experimental errors. Here, however, we cannot justify rounding off 1.51 to 1 or 2, but we can obtain a simple ratio by multiplying the relative amounts by two.

Now attempt the following exercises where you must decide whether to round off or multiply by a factor.

EXERCISE 20
Answer on page 113

A compound of carbon, hydrogen and oxygen contains 40.0% carbon, 6.6% hydrogen and 53.4% oxygen. Calculate its empirical formula.

EXERCISE 21
Answer on page 114

Determine the formula of a mineral with the following mass composition: Na = 12.1%, Al = 14.2%, Si = 22.1%, O = 42.1%, H_2O = 9.48%.

EXERCISE 22
Answer on page 114

A 10.00 g sample of a compound contains 3.91 g of carbon, 0.87 g of hydrogen and the remainder is oxygen. Calculate the empirical formula of the compound.

We now consider how we can use the mole concept for reactions taking place in solution.

5

AMOUNTS IN SOLUTION

So far we have shown how to calculate amount of substance from the mass of a substance and its molar mass. However, most chemical reactions take place in solution. If we want to know the amount of substance in solution, then we must know the concentration of the solution and its volume.

OBJECTIVES

When you have finished this chapter you should be able to:
■ define **concentration**;
■ explain the term **standard solution**;
■ calculate the concentration of a solution, given the amount or mass of solute and the volume of solution;
■ calculate the amount or mass of solute in a given volume of solution of known concentration.

■ 5.1 Concentration of solution

We express the concentration of a solution as the amount of solute dissolved in a given volume of solution; i.e.

$$\text{concentration} = \frac{\text{amount}}{\text{volume}} \quad \text{or, in symbols,} \quad c = \frac{n}{V}$$

Normally, we measure amount in mol, and volume in dm^3, so the usual unit of concentration is **mol dm^{-3}**.

■ 5.2 Standard solutions

A standard solution is one of known concentration. We can 'know' the concentration either by preparing the solution according to a given recipe or by analysing it.

Let us suppose we dissolve 0.15 mol (27.0 g) of glucose, $C_6H_{12}O_6$, in enough water to make 1.00 dm^3 of solution. Then its concentration is given as $c = 0.15$ mol dm^{-3}. The letter M is sometimes used as an abbreviation for mol dm^{-3}, but you should use it **only** in conjunction with a formula. For example, 0.0100 M NaOH means a solution of sodium hydroxide, NaOH, having a concentration of 0.0100 mol dm^{-3}.

In this chapter, we go through the main types of problems you are likely to meet which involve solutions. For each one, read the worked example, then try the exercises which follow it.

■ 5.3 Calculating concentration from volume and amount

WORKED EXAMPLE

Calculate the concentration of a solution which is made by dissolving 0.500 mol of sodium hydroxide, NaOH, in 200 cm^3 of solution.

Solution

Calculate the concentration by substituting into the key expression:

$$c = \frac{n}{V}$$

where $n = 0.500$ mol and $V = \left(\dfrac{200}{1000}\right) dm^3$.

$$c = \frac{n}{V} = \frac{0.500 \text{ mol}}{0.200 \text{ dm}^3} = 2.50 \text{ mol dm}^{-3}$$

Now attempt the following exercise.

EXERCISE 23

Answers on page 114

Assume that 0.100 mol of $CuSO_4\cdot5H_2O$ is placed in each of the volumetric flasks shown (Fig. 7) and is properly diluted to the volumes shown. Calculate the concentration of each solution.

Figure 7

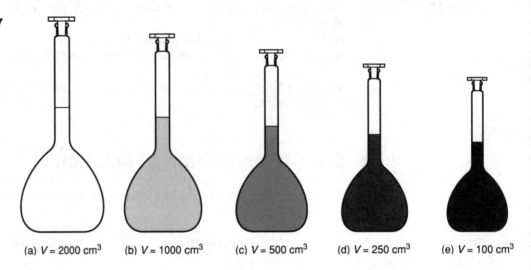

(a) $V = 2000$ cm^3 (b) $V = 1000$ cm^3 (c) $V = 500$ cm^3 (d) $V = 250$ cm^3 (e) $V = 100$ cm^3

■ 5.4 Calculating concentration from mass of solute and volume

Now we take this calculation a step further – be prepared for problems which give the mass of a substance, not the amount. These need an extra step at the start, i.e. dividing mass by molar mass to get amount using

$$n = \frac{m}{M}$$

Now attempt the following exercise.

EXERCISE 24

Answers on page 115

The table below indicates the masses of various compounds that were used to prepare the solutions of the stated volumes. Calculate the concentration of these solutions.

Table 2

Compound	Mass/g	Volume/cm^3
(a) $AgNO_3$	8.50	1000
(b) KIO_3	10.7	250
(c) $Pb(NO_3)_2$	11.2	50.0
(d) $K_2Cr_2O_7$	14.3	250
(e) $CuSO_4\cdot5H_2O$	11.9	500

You can now apply your knowledge of calculating concentrations to the preparation of a standard solution. Standard solutions are widely used in industrial research and teaching laboratories; it is important, therefore, that you should know how to prepare one.

OBJECTIVES

When you have finished this experiment you should be able to:
■ state the essential properties of a **primary standard**;
■ prepare a standard solution.

If possible, watch the ILPAC video programme 'Preparing a Standard Solution' which shows the techniques involved. Before you start, read the notes on this activity in the Introduction to ILPAC. If the videotape is not available, ask your teacher whether you have enough laboratory experience simply to follow the experimental instructions.

EXPERIMENT 2 Preparing a standard solution

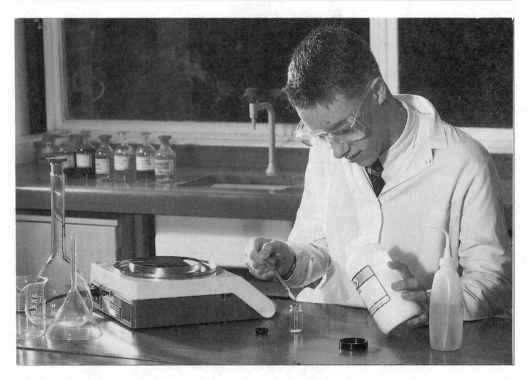

Aim The purpose of this experiment is to prepare a standard solution of potassium hydrogenphthalate.

Introduction Potassium hydrogenphthalate, $C_8H_5O_4K$, is a primary standard because it meets certain requirements.
- It must be available in a highly pure state.
- It must be stable in air.
- It must be easily soluble in water.
- It should have a high molar mass.
- In solution, when used in volumetric analysis, it must undergo complete and rapid reaction.

Weigh accurately a sample of potassium hydrogenphthalate and use it to make a solution of concentration close to 0.10 mol dm^{-3}. In Experiment 3 you use this solution to determine the concentration of a solution of sodium hydroxide.

Requirements
- safety spectacles
- weighing bottle
- spatula
- potassium hydrogenphthalate, $C_8H_5O_4K$
- access to a balance capable of weighing to within 0.01 g
- beaker, 250 cm³
- wash bottle of distilled water
- stirring rod with rubber end
- volumetric flask, 250 cm³, with label
- filter funnel
- dropping pipette

Procedure
1. Transfer between 4.8 g and 5.4 g of potassium hydrogenphthalate into a weighing bottle and weigh it to the nearest 0.01 g.
2. Put about 100 cm³ of distilled water into a 250 cm³ beaker. Carefully transfer the bulk of the potassium hydrogenphthalate from the weighing bottle into the beaker.
3. Reweigh the bottle with any remaining potassium hydrogenphthalate to the nearest 0.01 g.
4. Stir to dissolve the solid, using a glass rod with a flattened end. The solid will dissolve faster if you use the flattened end of the rod to grind the crystals to a smaller size. Press the rod down on the crystals and twist. Do **not** 'hammer' the crystals as this may crack the beaker! Stir rapidly and then wait for a few seconds; the undissolved crystals will collect in the centre and you can then repeat the process until all the solid has dissolved. Add some more distilled water if necessary. Rinse any remaining solution on the rod back into the beaker with a little water.
5. Transfer the solution to the volumetric flask through the filter funnel. Rinse the beaker well, making sure all the liquid goes into the volumetric flask.
6. Add distilled water, swirling at intervals to mix the contents but **not** inverting, until the level is within about 1 cm of the mark on the neck of the flask.
7. Using the dropping pipette, add enough water to bring the bottom of the meniscus to the mark as in Fig. 8. Insert the stopper and shake thoroughly ten times to ensure complete mixing. Simply inverting the flask once or twice does **not** mix the contents properly and is a very common fault.

Figure 8

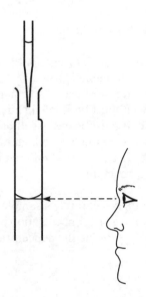

8. Label the flask with the contents, your name and the date. Leave a space for the concentration to be filled in after you have calculated it. Set aside the flask for Experiment 3 (in Part B).

Results and calculations

Using your data, you can fill in a copy of Results Table 3.

Results Table 3

Molar mass of potassium hydrogenphthalate, M	$g\ mol^{-1}$
Mass of bottle and contents before transfer, m_1	g
Mass of bottle and contents after transfer, m_2	g
Mass of potassium hydrogenphthalate, $m = (m_1 - m_2)$	g
Amount of potassium hydrogenphthalate, $n = m/M$	mol
Volume of solution, V	dm^3
Concentration of potassium hydrogenphthalate, $c = n/V$	$mol\ dm^{-3}$

(Specimen results on page 115.)

Questions

Answers on page 116

1. What effect would each of the errors described below have on the concentration of potassium hydrogenphthalate?
   a Some of the solid potassium hydrogenphthalate was spilled in making the transfer.
   b Not enough water was added to bring the volume up to the mark.

We now look at another type of calculation, but it is based on the same expression as are some of the problems you have already done.

■ 5.5 Calculating the amount of substance in a solution

Often you want to know the amount of substance contained in a given volume of solution of known concentration.

To do this you substitute values for c and V into the expression:

$$c = \frac{n}{V} \quad \text{in the form} \quad n = cV$$

You use this in the next exercise.

EXERCISE 25

Answers on page 116

Calculate the amount of solute in each of the following solutions:
a $4.00\ dm^3$ of 5.00 M NaOH,
b $1.00\ dm^3$ of 2.50 M HCl,
c $20.0\ cm^3$ of 0.439 M HNO_3.

Now we take this calculation a step further, calculating the mass of solute contained in a given volume of solution of known concentration. This needs an extra step at the finish, i.e. multiplying amount by molar mass to get mass $m = nM$.

Now try the next exercise.

EXERCISE 26

Answers on page 116

Calculate the mass of solute in the following solutions:
a $1.00\ dm^3$ of 0.100 M NaCl,
b $500\ cm^3$ of 1.00 M $CaCl_2$,
c $250\ cm^3$ of 0.200 M $KMnO_4$,
d $200\ cm^3$ of 0.117 M NaOH.

You have now reached the end of Part A of this unit. To revise for the test on the next page you may find it helpful to prepare a checklist of all the objectives or you may obtain this from your teacher.

■ Part A test

See the notes in the Introduction to ILPAC. To find out how well you have learned the material in Part A, try the test which follows. Read the notes below before starting.

■ You should spend about 40 minutes on this test.
■ You will need a data book.
■ Hand your answers to your teacher for marking.

1. What mass of material is there in each of the following?
   a 2.00 mol of SO_3
   b 0.0300 mol of Cl
   c 9.00 mol of $SO_4{}^{2-}$
   d 0.150 mol of $MgSO_4 \cdot 7H_2O$. (4)

2. What amount of each substance is contained in the following?
   a 31.0 g of P_4
   b 1.00×10^{22} atoms of Cu
   c 70.0 g of Fe^{2+}
   d 9.00×10^{24} molecules of C_2H_5OH. (4)

3. The mass of one molecule of a compound is 2.19×10^{-22} g. What is the molar mass of the compound? (2)

4. What mass of aluminium, Al, is required to produce 1000 g of iron, Fe, according to the equation:

$$3Fe_3O_4 \text{ (s)} + 8Al \text{ (s)} \rightarrow 4Al_2O_3 \text{ (s)} + 9Fe \text{ (s)} \ ?$$ (3)

5. A solution is made containing 2.38 g of magnesium chloride, $MgCl_2$, in 500 cm^3 of solution.
   a What is the concentration of magnesium chloride, $MgCl_2$, in this solution?
   b What is the concentration of chloride ions in this solution? (3)

6. A solution is made by dissolving 8.50 g of sodium nitrate, $NaNO_3$, and 16.40 g of calcium nitrate, $Ca(NO_3)_2$, in enough water to give 2000 cm^3 of solution.
   a What is the concentration of sodium ions in the solution?
   b What is the concentration of nitrate ions in the solution? (4)

7. A hydrated aluminium sulphate, $Al_2(SO_4)_3 \cdot xH_2O$, contains 8.10% of aluminium by mass. Find the value of x. (5)

(Total: 25 marks)

P
A
R
T

B

We now extend the concept of stoichiometry to reactions in solution, which you study by volumetric (titrimetric) analysis.

CHAPTER

6

VOLUMETRIC ANALYSIS (TITRIMETRY)

A titration is a laboratory procedure where a measured volume of one solution is added to a known volume of another reagent until the reaction is complete. This operation is an example of volumetric (titrimetric) analysis. The stoichiometric point (equivalence point) is usually shown by the colour change of an indicator, and is then known as the end-point.

Volumetric analysis is a powerful technique which is used in a variety of ways by chemists in many different fields.

You perform three types of titration in this unit:

■ an acid–base titration
■ a redox titration,
■ a precipitation titration.

You may wish to leave some or all of the experiments in this section until you have started on the next unit, Atomic Structure, which has few practicals. Ask your teacher about this.

OBJECTIVES When you have finished this chapter you should be able to:
■ calculate the concentration of a solution from titration data and the balanced equation;
■ perform titrations.

■ 6.1 Calculating the concentration of a solution from titration data

Before you do a titration, we give a Worked Example to illustrate titrimetric calculations. For the Worked Example, we use an acid–base titration, but the method is applicable to all titrations.

WORKED EXAMPLE We placed 20.0 cm^3 of a solution of barium hydroxide, Ba(OH)$_2$, of unknown concentration in a conical flask and titrated with a solution of hydrochloric acid, HCl, which has a concentration of 0.0600 mol dm^{-3}. The volume of acid required is 25.0 cm^3. Calculate the concentration of the barium hydroxide solution.

$$Ba(OH)_2 \text{ (aq)} + 2HCl \text{ (aq)} \rightarrow BaCl_2 \text{ (aq)} + 2H_2O \text{ (l)}$$

Solution This is a multi-step calculation. You may find it helpful to look again at the advice we gave on such calculations on page 17. A summarised 'flow-chart' for the solution to this problem is:

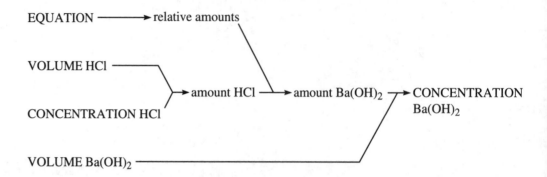

Now we look at the calculations, step by step.

1. Calculate the amount of HCl delivered (the solution of known concentration) by substitution into the expression

$$c = \frac{n}{V} \quad \text{in the form} \quad n = cV$$

where $c = 0.0600$ mol dm^{-3} and $V = (25.0/1000)$dm$^3 = 0.0250$ dm^3
∴ $n = cV = 0.0600$ mol dm$^{-3} \times 0.0250$ dm$^3 = 1.50 \times 10^{-3}$ mol

2. Calculate the amount of $Ba(OH)_2$ (the solution of unknown concentration) which reacts with this amount of HCl by substituting into the expression derived from the equation:

$$\frac{\text{amount of } Ba(OH)_2}{\text{amount of HCl}} = \frac{1}{2}$$

$$\therefore \text{amount of } Ba(OH)_2 = \frac{1}{2} \text{ amount of HCl*}$$

$$= \frac{1}{2}(1.50 \times 10^{-3} \text{ mol})$$

$$= 7.50 \times 10^{-4} \text{ mol}$$

(*Always check this step carefully – it is easy to put the '1/2' in the wrong place.)

3. Calculate the concentration of $Ba(OH)_2$ by substitution into the expression

$$c = \frac{n}{V}$$

where $n = 7.50 \times 10^{-4}$ mol and $V = 0.0200$ dm^3

$$\therefore c = \frac{n}{V} = \frac{7.50 \times 10^{-4} \text{ mol}}{0.0200 \text{ dm}^3} = 0.0375 \text{ mol dm}^{-3}$$

It is possible to derive a general expression to solve this problem and many like it. Remember, however, that you should not use an expression unless you understand its derivation.

■ 6.2 A general expression

Consider the general equation:

$$a \, A + b \, B \rightarrow \text{Products}$$

We can derive an expression relating concentration of A (c_A), concentration of B (c_B), volume of A (V_A), volume of B (V_B) and the stoichiometric coefficients a and b.
  We start with a relation obtained directly from the chemical equation. It is:

$$\frac{\text{amount of A}}{\text{amount of B}} = \frac{a}{b}$$

We know that:

$$\text{amount of A} = c_A V_A$$
$$\text{amount of B} = c_B V_B$$

So, substituting for amount of A and amount of B in the first expression gives:

$$\frac{c_A V_A}{c_B V_B} = \frac{a}{b}$$

To help you use this expression correctly, remember that both A and a are on the top and both B and b are on the bottom.
  This expression is very useful for solving titrimetric problems and we use it in our answers to such problems wherever appropriate. However, it may not **always** provide the **best** way to tackle a particular problem.
  Now we give you some practice in doing volumetric calculations.

EXERCISE 27
Answers on page 116

a Solve the Worked Example on page 29 using the expression we derived.
b Why is it not necessary to convert volumes in cm³ to dm³ when using the expression?

EXERCISE 28
Answers on page 117

What volume of sodium hydroxide solution, 0.500 M NaOH, is needed to neutralize
a 50.0 cm³ of nitric acid, 0.100 M HNO_3,

$$\text{NaOH (aq)} + \text{HNO}_3 \text{ (aq)} \rightarrow \text{NaNO}_3 \text{ (aq)} + \text{H}_2\text{O (l)}$$

b 22.5 cm³ of sulphuric acid, 0.262 M H_2SO_4,

$$2\text{NaOH (aq)} + \text{H}_2\text{SO}_4 \text{ (aq)} \rightarrow \text{Na}_2\text{SO}_4 \text{ (aq)} + 2\text{H}_2\text{O (l)}$$

Although you most often start your calculations knowing the equation for the reaction, you may sometimes have to derive the equation, as in the next exercise.

EXERCISE 29
Answers on page 117

As a result of a titration, it was found that 25.0 cm³ of silver nitrate solution, 0.50 M $AgNO_3$, reacted with 31.3 cm³ of barium chloride solution, 0.20 M $BaCl_2$. Use these results to determine the stoichiometric coefficients, a and b, in the equation:

$$a \, \text{AgNO}_3 \text{ (aq)} + b \, \text{BaCl}_2 \rightarrow \text{Products}$$

Now that you know how to use titration results in calculations you can perform a titration for yourself. The experimental techniques are worth studying before you begin.

The ILPAC video programme 'Performing a Titration' shows you the standard techniques of performing a titration. If possible you should watch this before you do the next experiment.

If the tape is not available, read about these techniques in a suitable book suggested by your teacher, or ask for a demonstration.

EXPERIMENT 3   An acid–base titration

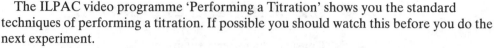

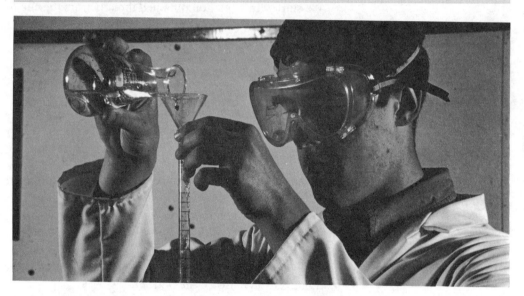

Aim   The purpose of this experiment is to determine the concentration of a solution of sodium hydroxide by titration against a standard solution of potassium hydrogenphthalate.

Introduction   You have already made a standard solution of potassium hydrogenphthalate, a primary standard. The substance has the formula $C_8H_5O_4K$, but because it behaves as a monoprotic (monobasic) acid in producing one mole of hydrogen ions per mole of compound, we can simplify the formula to HA. This simple formula is often used to represent an acid with a complicated structure.

Sodium hydroxide reacts with potassium hydrogenphthalate according to the equation:

(aq) + Na^+OH^- (aq) $\longrightarrow$ (aq) + H_2O

or

$$HA \text{ (aq)} + Na^+OH^- \text{ (aq)} \rightarrow Na^+A^- \text{ (aq)} + H_2O \text{ (l)}$$

To show you when the reaction is complete – the stoichiometric point or equivalence point – you use an indicator called phenolphthalein, which is colourless in acid and pink in alkaline solution. The point at which the addition of one drop (or even less) of alkali changes the solution from colourless to just faintly pink is called the end-point and, in this case, shows that the reaction is just complete.

Requirements
- safety spectacles
- filter funnel, small
- burette, 50 cm^3, and stand
- two beakers, 100 cm^3
- sodium hydroxide solution (approx. 0.1 M NaOH)
- pipette, 25 cm^3
- pipette filler
- standard potassium hydrogenphthalate solution (prepared in Experiment 2)
- four conical flasks, 250 cm^3
- phenolphthalein indicator solution
- white tile
- wash bottle of distilled water

HAZARD WARNING

Sodium hydroxide solution is very corrosive. Even when dilute it can damage your eyes. Therefore you **must**:
- **wear safety spectacles throughout the experiment.**

Procedure

1. Using the funnel, rinse the burette with the sodium hydroxide solution and fill it with the same solution. Do not forget to rinse and fill the tip. Record the initial burette reading in the 'Trial' column of Results Table 4.
2. Using a pipette filler, rinse the pipette with some of the potassium hydrogenphthalate solution and carefully transfer 25.0 cm^3 of the solution to a clean 250 cm^3 conical flask.
3. Add two to three drops of the phenolphthalein indicator solution.
4. Run sodium hydroxide solution from the burette into the flask, with swirling, until the solution just turns pink. This first flask may be used as a trial run, because you will probably overshoot the end-point. Record the final burette reading.
5. Refill the burette with the sodium hydroxide solution, and again record the initial burette reading to the nearest 0.05 cm^3 (one drop).
6. Using the pipette, transfer 25.0 cm^3 of the potassium hydrogenphthalate solution to another clean conical flask. Add two to three drops of the phenolphthalein solution.
7. Carefully titrate this solution to the end-point, adding the alkali drop by drop when you think the colour is about to change.
8. Repeat steps 5, 6 and 7 at least twice more.
9. Empty the burette and wash it carefully immediately after the titration, especially if it has a ground glass tap.

Accuracy

You should record burette readings to the nearest 0.05 cm^3 (approximately one drop). Consecutive titrations should agree to within 0.10 cm^3 and, strictly, you should repeat the titration until this is achieved. However, you may have neither the time nor the materials to do this. With practice, your technique will improve so that it is not necessary to do more than four titrations. Calculate the mean of the two (or preferably three) closest consecutive readings and quote this also to the nearest 0.05 cm^3. This does not introduce a fourth significant figure; it merely makes the third figure more reliable.

Results Table 4

Pipette solution						mol dm^{-3}	cm^3
Burette solution						mol dm^{-3}	
Indicator							
		Trial	1	2	3	(4)	
Burette readings	Final						
	Initial						
Volume used (titre)/cm^3							
Mean titre/cm^3							

Calculation

Specimen results on page 118

1. Calculate the concentration of the sodium hydroxide solution.

Questions

Answers on page 118

1. What effect would each of the errors described below have on the calculated value of the concentration of sodium hydroxide?
   a The burette is not rinsed with the sodium hydroxide solution.
   b The pipette is not rinsed with the potassium hydrogenphthalate solution.
   c The tip of the burette is not filled before titration begins.
   d The conical flask contains some distilled water before the addition of potassium hydrogenphthalate.
2. In using phenolphthalein as an indicator, we prefer to titrate from a colourless to pink solution rather than from pink to colourless. Suggest a reason for this.
3. Why is it advisable to remove sodium hydroxide from the burette as soon as possible after the titration?

In the next experiment, you perform another titration but this time you titrate a solution of an oxidant into a solution of a reductant. This type of titration is called a redox titration.

OBJECTIVE   When you have finished this experiment you should be able to:
■ use titration data to determine the **stoichiometry of a reaction.**

EXPERIMENT 4   A redox titration

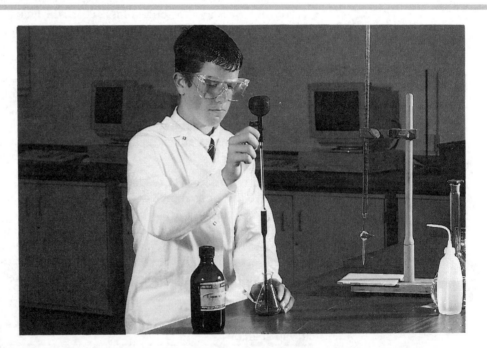

Aim   The purpose of this experiment is to balance the equation for the reaction between sodium thiosulphate and iodine.

$$a \, Na_2S_2O_3 \, (aq) + b \, I_2 \, (aq) \rightarrow Products$$

Introduction   You are to determine the ratio of a to b and so determine the stoichiometry of the reaction. You do this by taking a known amount of iodine and titrating it with standard sodium thiosulphate.

The indicator that you use in this titration is starch solution, which is deep blue in the presence of iodine; it is added near the end of the titration when the solution is straw-coloured. If you add starch too soon, you may get a blue-black precipitate which does not dissolve again easily even though there is an excess of thiosulphate. The end-point in this titration is the point at which the addition of one drop of sodium thiosulphate causes the disappearance of the deep-blue colour.

Requirements

- safety spectacles
- filter funnel
- burette, 50 cm^3, and stand
- two beakers, 100 cm^3
- sodium thiosulphate solution, standardised
- pipette, 10 cm^3
- pipette filler
- iodine solution, standardised
- four conical flasks, 250 cm^3
- starch indicator solution
- white tile
- wash bottle of distilled water

Procedure

1. Using the funnel, rinse the burette and tip with the sodium thiosulphate solution. Fill it with the same solution. Don't forget to fill the tip. Record the initial burette reading in Results Table 5.
2. Rinse the pipette with some of the iodine solution and carefully transfer 10.0 cm^3 of the solution to one of the conical flasks.
3. Titrate this solution until the colour of the iodine has **almost** gone (as indicated by a pale straw colour).
4. Add 1–2 cm^3 of starch solution and continue the titration, adding sodium thiosulphate dropwise until the end-point. Use the first flask for a trial run. Record the final burette reading.
5. Repeat the titration three more times. Enter your results into a copy of Results Table 5. These titrations should agree to within 0.10 cm^3.

Results Table 5

Pipette solution						mol dm^{-3}	cm^3
Burette solution						mol dm^{-3}	
Indicator							
		Trial	1	2	3	(4)	
Burette readings	Final						
	Initial						
Volume used (titre)/cm^3							
Mean titre/cm^3							

Calculation

Specimen results on page 118

1. Use your results to determine the stoichiometric coefficients, a and b, in the equation:

$$a\ Na_2S_2O_3\ (aq) + b\ I_2\ (aq) \rightarrow Products$$

2. All the iodine forms sodium iodide, NaI. There is one other product – work out its formula.

In the next experiment you perform another titration, where you titrate a solution of silver nitrate into a solution of a halide. This type of titration is called a precipitation titration.

When you have finished this experiment you should be able to:
■ determine the number of molecules of water of hydration from titration data.

 In this experiment, you make a standard solution of barium chloride. If you do not remember the technique, watch the ILPAC video programme 'Preparing a Standard Solution' or re-read the instructions given in Experiment 2. The ILPAC video programme 'Performing a Titration' also shows you the colour change to look for at the end-point.

EXPERIMENT 5 A precipitation titration

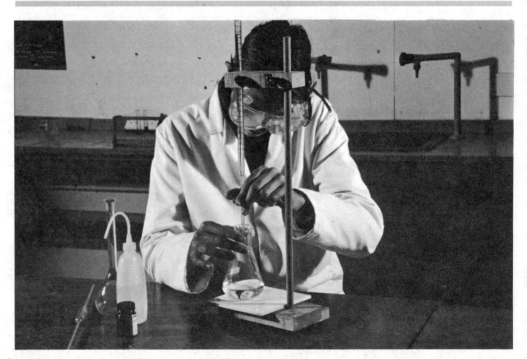

Aim The purpose of this experiment is to determine the number of molecules of water of hydration in hydrated barium chloride, i.e. to calculate the value of x in the formula $BaCl_2 \cdot xH_2O$.

Introduction You titrate chloride ions with silver ions, according to the equation:

$$Ag^+ (aq) + Cl^- (aq) \rightarrow AgCl (s)$$

This provides you with the data necessary to do the calculations. The indicator for the titration is potassium chromate(VI). When all the chloride ions have reacted, any more silver ions react with the indicator producing a red precipitate of silver chromate(VI). This is because silver chloride is less soluble than silver chromate(VI).

$$2Ag^+ (aq) + CrO_4^{2-} (aq) \rightarrow Ag_2CrO_4 (s)$$

The end-point in this reaction is when one drop of silver ion solution produces a red tinge on the precipitate of silver chloride.

Barium ions also react with chromate ions so the barium must be removed by adding sulphate ions:

$$Ba^{2+} (aq) + SO_4^{2-} (aq) \rightarrow BaSO_4 (s)$$

This does not affect the concentration of chloride ions.

Requirements
- safety spectacles
- weighing bottle
- spatula
- barium chloride crystals
- access to balance capable of weighing to 0.01 g
- beaker, 250 cm^3
- wash bottle of distilled water
- stirring rod with rubber end
- volumetric flask, 250 cm^3, with label
- filter funnel
- dropping pipette
- burette, 50 cm^3, and stand
- two beakers, 100 cm^3
- silver nitrate solution, standardised
- pipette, 10 cm^3
- pipette filler
- four conical flasks, 250 cm^3
- sodium sulphate
- potassium chromate solution
- 'silver residues' bottle

HAZARD WARNING

Barium chloride is harmful if swallowed. Silver nitrate is corrosive and can stain the skin. Therefore you **must**:
- **use the pipette filler provided;**
- **wash your hands after use.**

Procedure

1. Prepare a standard solution of hydrated barium chloride by accurately weighing out between 1.4 g and 1.6 g of the salt. Dissolve this and make up to 250 cm^3 in a volumetric flask. Fill in a copy of Results Table 6.
2. Rinse the burette with some silver nitrate solution and fill. Don't forget the tip.
3. Rinse the 10.0 cm^3 pipette with barium chloride solution, and transfer 10.0 cm^3 to a conical flask.
4. Add about 1 g of sodium sulphate crystals to the flask and swirl it.
5. Add two to three drops of potassium chromate(VI) indicator. Titrate the solution to the end-point, as shown by the first appearance of a permanent but faint reddish precipitate of silver chromate(VI). Use the first flask for a trial run. Enter your results in a copy of Results Table 7.
6. Repeat steps 2–5 three times. Don't wash the contents of the titration flasks down the sink – pour them into a 'silver residue' bottle.

Results and calculations
Results Table 6

Mass of bottle and contents before transfer, m_1	g
Mass of bottle and contents after transfer, m_2	g
Mass of sample, $m = (m_1 - m_2)$	g
Mass of BaCl$_2 \cdot x$H$_2$O in 10.0 cm^3 of solution	g

Results Table 7

Pipette solution				mol dm^{-3}			cm^3
Burette solution				mol dm^{-3}			
Indicator							
		Trial	1	2	3	(4)	
Burette readings	Final						
	Initial						
Volume used (titre)/cm^3							
Mean titre/cm^3							

Calculation

Specimen results on page 120

1. From the mean titre and concentration of silver nitrate, calculate the amount of chloride ions present in a 10.0 cm^3 sample.
2. Calculate the mass of anhydrous barium chloride, $BaCl_2$, present in a sample.
3. Calculate the mass of water present by subtracting the mass of $BaCl_2$ from the mass of $BaCl_2 \cdot x H_2O$.
4. Determine the ratio of amount of $BaCl_2$ to amount of H_2O and thus the value of x.

A flow-chart for this multi-step calculation is as follows:

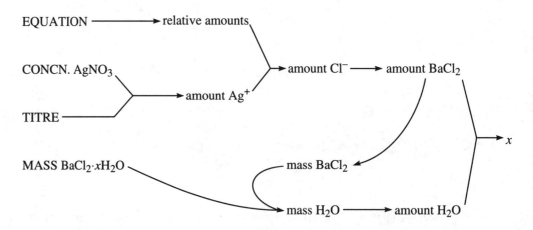

The calculation in the last experiment should help you to do the next exercise, which is part of an A-level question. We suggest that if you find it difficult, you look at our introduction to the Worked Example on page 17 and sketch out a flow-chart before you begin.

EXERCISE 30

Answers on page 120

When 0.203 g of hydrated magnesium chloride, $MgCl_m \cdot n H_2O$, was dissolved in water and titrated with 0.100 M silver nitrate ($AgNO_3$) solution, 20.0 cm^3 of the latter was required. A sample of the hydrated chloride lost 53.2% of its mass when heated in a stream of hydrogen chloride, leaving a residue of anhydrous magnesium chloride. From these figures, calculate the values of m and n.

■ End-of-unit test (a practical test)

 To test both your practical skill and your ability to calculate, we base the End-of-unit test on an experiment. (In all other units, the tests are written, but a practical test is appropriate for this unit.)

Let your teacher know when you are ready for the test.

Aim   The purpose of this experiment is to determine x in the formula $Fe(NH_4)_2(SO_4)_2 \cdot xH_2O$ by titration against a standard solution of potassium manganate(VII) (permanganate). The directions are similar to those that would be given by an examination board.

A is a solution of ammonium iron(II) sulphate, $Fe(NH_4)_2(SO_4)_2 \cdot xH_2O$, the precise concentration of which (in g dm^{-3}) is given by the teacher.

B is a solution of potassium manganate(VII), $KMnO_4$ (permanganate), the precise concentration of which (in mol dm^{-3}) is given by the teacher.

Results Table 8

Pipette solution				mol dm^{-3}	cm^3
Burette solution				mol dm^{-3}	
Indicator					
		Trial	1	2	3	(4)
Burette readings	Final					
	Initial					
Volume used (titre)/cm^3						
Mean titre/cm^3						

Procedure   Pipette 25 cm^3 of the ammonium iron(II) sulphate solution, A, into a conical flask and add an equal volume of dilute sulphuric acid. Titrate with potassium manganate(VII) solution, B, until a permanent faint pink colour appears. Repeat the titration twice and enter your results in a copy of Results Table 8.

The overall equation for the reaction is

$$MnO_4^-\ (aq) + 5Fe^{2+}\ (aq) + 8H^+\ (aq) \rightarrow Mn^{2+}\ (aq) + 5Fe^{3+}\ (aq) + 4H_2O\ (l)$$

Calculation   Use your results to determine x in the formula $Fe(NH_4)_2(SO_4)_2 \cdot xH_2O$. You should set out your calculations so that every step in your working is clearly shown. If you cannot work out a method of calculation, use the suggestions below.

Hand your results table and calculations to your teacher for marking.

Calculation steps   1. From the titre and the equation for the reaction calculate the concentration of Fe^{2+} ions.
2. From the concentration calculate the mass of anhydrous $Fe(NH_4)_2(SO_4)_2$ in one litre of solution.
3. Subtract the mass obtained in step 2 from the mass of the salt in one litre. This difference, z g, divided by 18 g mol^{-1} gives the amount of water of crystallization in y mol of the salt, where y mol dm^{-3} is the concentration calculated in step 1.
4. x mol is the amount of water in 1 mol of the salt, i.e.

$$x = \frac{z}{18} \times \frac{1}{y}$$

PHYSICOCHEMICAL QUANTITIES AND UNITS

Any substance or object has physical properties such as length, mass, energy and so on, which we can measure by comparing with some other substance or object. For example, we can measure length using a ruler or mass by using standard masses (or 'weights') and the measurement is made by counting the ratio between the length or mass of the object and the length or mass of the standard.

A physical quantity is expressed as the product of a number and a unit. For example, the length of a laboratory bench could be stated as 9.00 feet or 108 inches or 2.74 metres. The numbers and units may change but the product, i.e. the length of the bench, is fixed. In scientific work it is preferable, although not compulsory, to use SI units.* We could, for example, say that the length of the bench is 1.80 teachers, so long as we specify precisely what one 'teacher' is in the appropriate SI unit (metre) but on the whole it is usually better to stick to SI units.

Figure 9

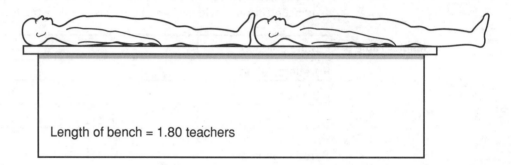

Length of bench = 1.80 teachers

The expression 'physical quantity = number × unit' can be altered to 'physical quantity/unit = number' and you will find that columns of figures in your data book are headed in this way. For example, molar masses of substances are headed by 'M/g mol^{-1}'. Axes of graphs should be labelled in the same way. For example, a graph of temperature against time could have the horizontal axis labelled 'time/s' or 'time/min'. In some older textbooks you may see such graphs labelled 'time (sec)'; this is quite illogical since in a mathematical context $x(y)$ means x multiplied by y, whereas what is being plotted is time divided by seconds.

■ Symbols

In SI the symbols for physical quantities are printed in italic (sloping) letters whereas symbols for units are printed in roman (upright) letters. This convention is followed in the ILPAC units and you should try to cultivate the habit of doing the same. For example, m stands for mass but m stands for metres. If you can get used to this, then not only will it avoid confusion but also it will please those kindly people, the GCE A-level examiners!

■ Calculations involving physical quantities

Calculation is usually done by substituting values into an equation. It is important to get into the habit of substituting both the numbers and the units. Perform the arithmetic (using a calculator or otherwise), then combine the units to produce the correct units for the answer. To make this clear study some of the Worked Examples.

*SI = 'Système Internationale d'Unites' or International System of Units. Your data book will probably give a brief description of the SI and its advantages.

SIGNIFICANT FIGURES AND SCIENTIFIC MEASUREMENTS

These notes on the use of significant figures are not rigorous. We merely give some useful rules which you can apply to ordinary A-level calculations. For a detailed treatment you can read a textbook on the theory of measurements.

The numerical value of any physical measurement is an approximation which is limited by the accuracy of the measuring instrument.

Generally, the last digit in a measured quantity has an uncertainty associated with it. For example, in reading a thermometer, part of which is shown in Fig. 10, some may read the temperature as 21.1°C and some may read it as 21.2°C or 21.3°C.

Figure 10

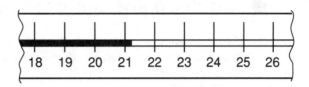

That is, there is no doubt that the temperature is between 21 and 22 degrees Celsius, but there is some uncertainty in the last place. It is for this reason that we must consider the use of significant figures. Furthermore, it is important to consider the use of significant figures when so many calculations are made using electronic calculators which give as many as ten digits on their displays. You are very rarely justified in using all of them.

■ Zeros

A measured mass of 23 g has two significant figures, 2 and 3. If this same mass is written as 0.023 kg, it still contains two significant figures because zeros appearing as the first figures of a number are not significant – they merely locate the decimal point. However, the mass 0.0230 kg is expressed to three significant figures (2, 3 and the last 0).

The expression 'the length is 4700 m' does not necessarily show the accuracy of the measurement. To do this, the number should be written in standard form. If the measurement is made only to the nearest 1000 m, we use only one significant figure, i.e. $l = 5 \times 10^3$ m.

A more precise measurement, to the nearest 100 m, merits two significant figures, i.e. $l = 4.7 \times 10^3$ m, and so on as summarised in Table 3.

Table 3

Distance l/m	Significant figures	Range of uncertainty	Precision of measurement
4700	unspecified	unspecified	unspecified
5×10^3	1	4.5 to 5.5	nearest 1000 m
4.7×10^3	2	4.65 to 4.75	nearest 100 m
4.70×10^3	3	4.695 to 4.705	nearest 10 m
4.700×10^3	4	4.6995 to 4.7005	nearest 1 m

Here is an exercise to see if you can recognise the number of significant figures in a measured quantity.

EXERCISE 31

Answers on page 122

How many significant figures are in the following quantities?

a 2.54 g,
b 2.205 g,
c 1.1 g,
d 14.0 cm^3,
e 1.86×10^5 s,

f 2.0070 g,
g 9.993 g cm^{-3},
h 5070 m s^{-1},
i 127 000 kg.

Now we look at significant figures in the results of combining uncertain values in calculations.

■ Addition and subtraction

After addition or subtraction, the answer should be rounded off to keep only the same number of decimal places as the **least** precise item. Here are some Worked Examples.

WORKED EXAMPLE   Add the following quantities:

a
$$\begin{array}{r} 46.247 \text{ cm}^3 \\ 3.219 \text{ cm}^3 \\ \underline{0.224 \text{ cm}^3} \\ 49.690 \text{ cm}^3 \end{array}$$ Answer: 49.690 cm^3

Each volume to be added is expressed to the nearest 0.001 cm^3, so we can express the answer also to the nearest 0.001 cm^3.

b
$$\begin{array}{r} 26.6 \quad \text{ cm}^3 \\ 0.0028 \text{ cm}^3 \\ \underline{0.00002 \text{ cm}^3} \\ 26.60282 \text{ cm}^3 \end{array}$$ Answer: 26.6 cm^3

The number 26.6 is expressed to one place past the decimal point so you cannot have the answer quoted to a greater accuracy than one place past the decimal point.

c
$$\begin{array}{r} 2.40 \quad \text{ cm}^3 \\ 3.6584 \text{ cm}^3 \\ \underline{0.029 \quad \text{ cm}^3} \\ 6.0874 \text{ cm}^3 \end{array}$$ Answer: 6.09 cm^3

The reasoning here is the same as in part **b**. The least accurate measurement is 2.40 cm^3 so, in the answer, the volume cannot be quoted to more than two places past the decimal point. In this case, however, we round up rather than round down.
   The reasoning is the same for subtraction.

WORKED EXAMPLE   Perform the following subtractions:

a
$$\begin{array}{r} 7.26 \text{ g} \\ - \ 0.2 \quad \text{g} \\ \hline 7.06 \quad \text{g} \end{array}$$ Answer: 7.1 g

b
$$\begin{array}{r} 539.27 \text{ g} \\ - \ 12.8 \quad \text{g} \\ \hline 526.47 \quad \text{g} \end{array}$$ Answer: 526.5 g

Try the following exercises:

EXERCISE 32

Answers on page 122

Add the following, expressing your answer to the correct number of significant figures:

a

$$
\begin{array}{rl}
203 & \text{g} \\
4 & \text{g} \\
\underline{0.77} & \text{g}
\end{array}
$$

b

$$
\begin{array}{rl}
0.0034 & \text{dm}^3 \\
0.094 & \text{dm}^3 \\
\underline{0.552} & \text{dm}^3
\end{array}
$$

EXERCISE 33

Answers on page 122

Perform the following subtractions:

a

$$
\begin{array}{rl}
4.0 & \text{m} \\
\underline{-\,0.623} & \text{m}
\end{array}
$$

b

$$
\begin{array}{rl}
76 & \text{cm}^3 \\
\underline{-\,0.3} & \text{cm}^3
\end{array}
$$

The rules for multiplication and division are even easier.

■ Multiplication and division

The result of multiplying or dividing can contain only as many significant figures as are contained in the factor with the least number of significant figures.

WORKED EXAMPLE

Calculate the density of an object which weighs 17.32 g and has a volume of 2.4 cm^3.

Solution

$$
\text{density} = \frac{\text{mass}}{\text{volume}} = \frac{17.32\ \text{g}}{2.4\ \text{cm}^3}
$$

A calculator gives the result as 7.2166667 g cm^{-3}. But the volume has the smaller number of significant figures – two. So the result is rounded off to 7.2 g cm^{-3}.

Now do the next exercise.

EXERCISE 34

Answers on page 122

Multiply the following, expressing your answer to the correct number of significant figures:
a 0.11 mol dm^{-3} × 0.0272 dm^3
b 2.43 mol × 27.9 g mol^{-1}

EXERCISE 35

Answers on page 122

Divide the following, expressing your answer to the correct number of significant figures:

a

$$
\frac{9.2\ \text{g}}{19.00\ \text{g mol}^{-1}}
$$

b

$$
\frac{0.20\ \text{g}}{0.1\ \text{cm}^3}
$$

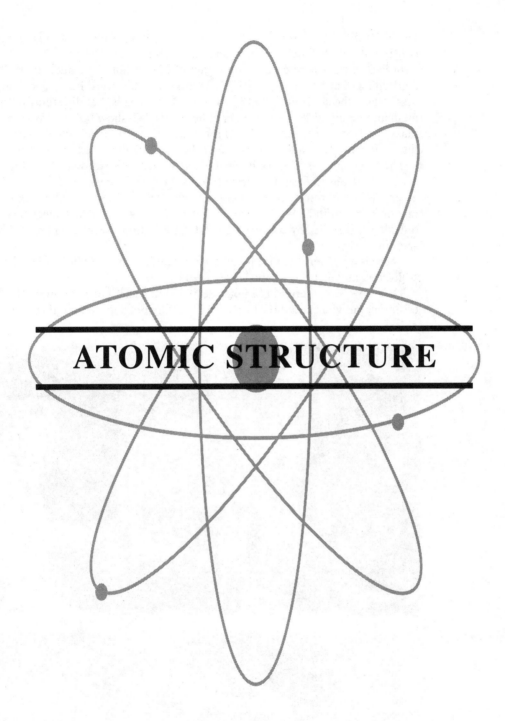

ATOMIC STRUCTURE

INTRODUCTION

Elements differ from one another because they have different atoms. Every atom consists of a central nucleus surrounded by electrons.

In Part A we describe the composition of the nucleus. The nucleus can be regarded as a grouping of even smaller particles: protons and neutrons. For a given element, all atoms have the same number of protons in the nucleus, but different isotopes of the element contain different numbers of neutrons. We show how an instrument called the mass spectrometer gives us a lot of information about nuclei. We also describe how nuclei decompose (radioactivity) and other aspects of nuclear chemistry.

The total number of extra-nuclear electrons (i.e. electrons surrounding the nucleus) also varies from element to element. In Part B, we describe how these electrons are arranged in different shells, and how a shell may have several sub-shells consisting of one or more orbitals. We present evidence for the way in which electrons are arranged outside the nucleus, by considering, firstly, ionisation energies and secondly, emission spectra.

There is an experiment in the unit – a qualitative examination of spectra of some s-block elements using a hand spectroscope.

There are two video programmes designed to accompany this unit. Their use is not essential, but you should try to see them at the appropriate time if they are available.

Instrumental techniques.

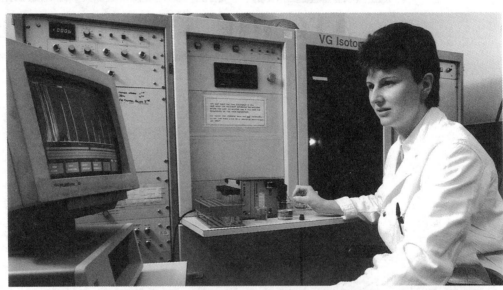

Using a spectrometer.

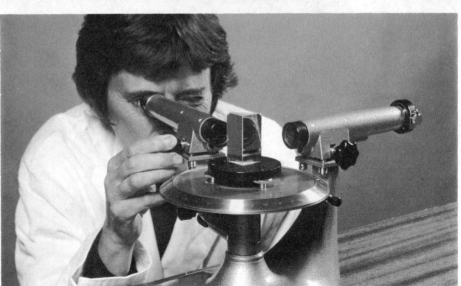

■ Pre-knowledge

Before you start work on this unit you should be able to:

1. Explain each of the following terms:
   a element,
   b atom,
   c ion,
   d relative atomic mass,
   e mole,
   f the Avogadro constant, *L,*
   g frequency,
   h wavelength.
2. State the relative masses and charges of the three fundamental particles in the atom.
3. Describe, at a simple level, a planetary model of the atom, using the terms: proton, neutron, electron, nucleus, shell (or orbit).
4. Write down the names, symbols and atomic numbers of the first 20 elements in the Periodic Table.
5. Write out the electron arrangements of the first 20 elements in the Periodic Table, using the style: Na – 2.8.1.
6. Write equations for the formation of ions from atoms.

   To find out whether you are ready to start Part A, try the following test, which is based on the pre-knowledge items. You should not spend more than 30 minutes on this test. Hand your answers to your teacher for marking.

■ Pre-test

1. Copy and complete Table 4 to summarise the properties of the three fundamental particles found in an atom.

Table 4

Fundamental particle	Relative mass	Relative charge
Proton		
Neutron		
Electron		

(6)

2. Identify the numbered elements in the following extract of the Periodic Table.

Figure 11

Li	Be	B	(1)	N	O	F	(2)
(3)	Mg	Al	Si	P	(4)	Cl	Ar
K	(5)						

(5)

3. The electron configuration of magnesium is represented by 2.8.2. Write the corresponding configurations for:
   a lithium,
   b nitrogen,
   c silicon.

(3)

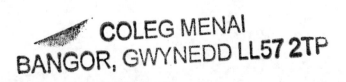
COLEG MENAI
BANGOR, GWYNEDD LL57 2TP

4. The way in which potassium normally ionises is represented by:

$$K \rightarrow K^+ + e^-$$

Write similar equations for the ionisation of:
a magnesium,
b chlorine,
c oxygen. (6)

5. Explain why neon does not ionise in normal chemical reactions. (1)

6. Which of the following statements about an atom is not true?
The atomic number Z represents:
a the number of electrons going round the nucleus,
b the positive charge on the nucleus,
c the number of neutrons in the nucleus,
d the element's position in the periodic table. (1)

7. Figure 12 represents a generalised form of radiation

Figure 12

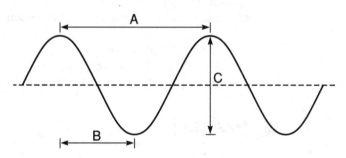

Which letter represents the wavelength of the radiation? (1)

8. Radiation is often identified by its frequency. Which of the following are units of frequency?
a cm s^{-1},
b m s^{-2},
c s^{-1},
d m s^{-1},
e min^{-1}. (2)

(Total: 25 marks)

PART A

THE NUCLEUS

We start this unit by considering the size of an average atom and the relative size of its nucleus.

CHAPTER 7

RELATIVE SIZES

OBJECTIVE   When you have finished this chapter you should be able to:
■ appreciate the approximate size of an atom and the relative sizes of an atom and its nucleus.

■ 7.1 How big is an atom?

Atomic size obviously varies from element to element. Radii lie within the range 0.05–0.20 nm.* The following exercise helps you to appreciate how small this is.

EXERCISE 36
Answers on page 123

Suppose a football, diameter 22 cm, is scaled up so that it becomes as big as the earth, diameter 13 000 km. Calculate whether an atom of diameter 0.32 nm will become as big as:

a a pin-head, diameter 1 mm,
b a 1p piece, diameter 1.9 cm,
c a football, diameter 22 cm,
d a weather balloon, diameter 1.8 m.

■ 7.2 How big is the nucleus?

An atom is small, but its nucleus is smaller still. While the radius of an atom is of the order of 10^{-10} m, that of a nucleus is of the order of 10^{-15} m. Do the next exercise to help you appreciate the difference in size.

EXERCISE 37
Answers on page 123

If the nucleus of an atom were scaled up to the size of a pin-head (say 1 mm diameter), how big would the atom be?

Since the mass of an atom is concentrated in its nucleus, the nucleus must be extremely dense. It follows also that most of the volume of an atom is almost empty space, being occupied by electrons that have very small mass compared to that of a nucleus.

Most of your body is empty space too. If all the spaces between the nuclei were squeezed out, you would be only half as big as a flea, although your weight would be the same.

In view of this, you may be wondering why any object appears solid. The electrons in an atom move very rapidly around the nucleus, somewhere within a particular radius. The electrons effectively form a shield around the nucleus, marking the limits of the atom's volume and making it seem solid.

You now go on to revise atomic number and mass number and find out more about isotopes.

*One nanometre, nm = 10^{-9} m (*nano* comes from the Greek word meaning dwarf).

ATOMIC NUMBER, MASS NUMBER AND ISOTOPES

Atomic number and mass number give us important information about an atom and are particularly useful in distinguishing one isotope of an element from another.

OBJECTIVES

When you have finished this chapter you should be able to:
- define the terms **atomic number**, Z, and **mass number**, A;
- explain what **isotopes** are;
- use values for atomic number and mass number to calculate **the number of protons** and **neutrons** in the nucleus;
- use **isotopic symbols** to describe the composition of a nucleus, e.g. $^{12}_{6}C$.

Read about atomic number and mass number in your textbook(s), and find out what isotopes are. See notes on reading in the Introduction to ILPAC.

You should now be able to answer Exercises 38 and 39.

EXERCISE 38
Answers on page 123

Define the terms atomic number and mass number.

EXERCISE 39
Answers on page 123

Explain what isotopes are, using nitrogen as an example.

Now that you have revised these terms, go on to the next exercise, which is part of an A-level structured question.

EXERCISE 40
Answers on page 123

The table shows the mass number and number of neutrons in the nucleus, for four atoms, W, X, Y and Z.

	W	X	Y	Z
Mass number	36	39	40	40
Neutrons in nucleus	18	20	21	22

a Write down the atomic numbers of the four atoms.
b Which of the four atoms are isotopes of the same element?

We end this chapter by revising a shorthand way of showing the composition of an isotope.

■ 8.1 Isotopic symbols

You may already have met a shorthand description of an atom; the mass number is shown as a superscript before the symbol and the atomic number as a subscript. In this way, $^{27}_{13}Al$ is a description of the aluminium atom. To make sure that you can use this convention correctly, try the next exercise.

EXERCISE 41
Answers on page 123

a Use your data book* to identify the stable isotopes of the following elements:
i) Ar,   ii) Cu,   iii) Si.
Describe each one, using isotopic symbols.
b Write down the number of neutrons in the nucleus of each isotope.

In the next chapter, we look at the mass spectrometer and how it can be used to find the relative atomic masses of elements with several isotopes.

*If you haven't used your data book to look up information about isotopes before, try either 'isotopes, stable, abundance' or 'nuclide, abundance' in the index. Abundance means the percentage of an isotope that occurs in nature and nuclide is a general word used to refer to any atom or ion having a particular nucleus.

THE MASS SPECTROMETER

In the first unit, you learned how to calculate relative atomic mass on the carbon-12 scale. In this chapter, you find out how relative atomic mass can be measured using a mass spectrometer. This instrument is also important for measuring the relative molecular masses of compounds, particularly organic ones, and determining their molecular structure.

OBJECTIVES

When you have finished this chapter you should be able to:
■ describe the principal parts of a **mass spectrometer** and explain their functions;
■ explain how the deflection of a beam of ions by a magnetic field depends on the masses and the charges of the ions.

If the ILPAC video programme 'Instrumental Methods' is available, you should now watch the section on the mass spectrometer. Don't spend time viewing the whole video at this point; your teacher will guide you to the appropriate section.

Whether or not you view the video programme, you should now go on to read about the mass spectrometer.

■ 9.1 The instrument

Look up 'mass spectrometer' in your textbook and read the section on it, bearing in mind the above objectives. You may also come across '**mass spectrograph**'. This instrument works on the same principle as the mass spectrometer – the only difference is the way in which the ions are detected. When you have finished the reading, do the next two exercises.

EXERCISE 42
Answers on page 123

a Make a copy of Fig. 13, which is a diagram of a mass spectrometer.

Figure 13 The mass spectrometer.

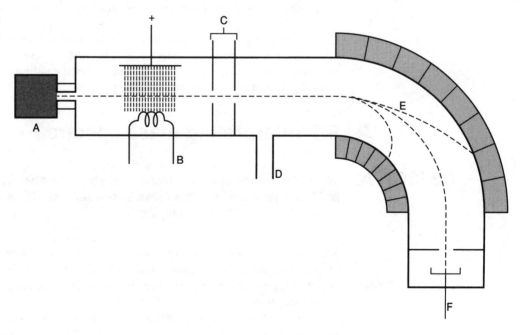

b Label the parts A to F.
c Describe the function of, or process occurring in, each of these parts.

EXERCISE 43

Answers on page 124

The isotopic composition of the gas radon was investigated using a mass spectrometer, part of which is shown in Fig. 14.

Figure 14

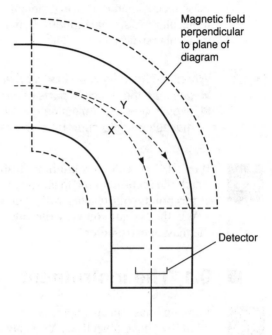

Magnetic field perpendicular to plane of diagram

Detector

a Radon has two isotopes, $^{222}_{86}Rn$ and $^{220}_{86}Rn$.
  i) Write the formulae of the two singly-charged ions that would form in the instrument.
  ii) State which ion will follow the path marked X on the diagram.
b Mention two adjustments that could be made to the instrument to bring the ions from Y onto the detector.
c If Rn^{2+} ions were to form in the instrument, would you expect them to be deflected less than or more than the ions at X and Y?

Having established how a mass spectrometer works, we go on to interpret the information it records, known as a mass spectrum. You may also find the names 'mass spectrometer trace' or 'mass spectrogram' in your reading. These mean exactly the same. Spectrum is a Latin word and its plural is 'spectra'.

■ 9.2 Interpreting mass spectra

OBJECTIVE

When you have finished this section you should be able to:
■ identify peaks on a simple **mass spectrum** and use them to calculate the relative abundances and masses of ions.

When a beam of ions strikes the detector in a mass spectrometer, it produces an electrical impulse, which is amplified and fed into a recorder. The mass of the isotope and its relative abundance are then shown by a peak on the chart. A set of such peaks is a mass spectrum.

Figure 15 shows a mass spectrum for rubidium. The horizontal axis shows the mass/charge ratio of the ions entering the detector. If it is assumed that all the ions carry a single positive charge, the horizontal axis can also be labelled 'mass number', 'isotopic mass' or 'relative atomic mass'. The vertical axis shows the abundance of the ions. It can be labelled 'detector current', 'relative abundance' or 'ion intensity'.

Figure 15

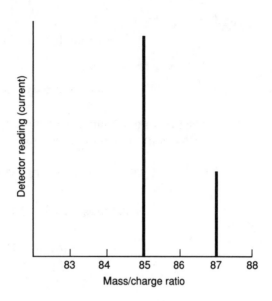

EXERCISE 44
Answers on page 124

EXERCISE 44

Refer to Fig. 15 to answer this question.

a Describe the two isotopes of rubidium using isotopic symbols.

b What information do you get from the heights of the peaks on the mass spectrum?

In the next section we go on to use the information from mass spectra to calculate the relative atomic mass of an element.

■ 9.3 Calculating the relative atomic mass of an element

OBJECTIVES

When you have finished this section you should be able to:

■ use a mass spectrum to calculate the **relative atomic mass** of an element;

■ use percentage abundance data to calculate the relative atomic mass of an element;

■ sketch a mass spectrum, given relevant data.

We start this section with a Worked Example, using the mass spectrum shown in Fig. 15. Read through it and then try the exercise which follows:

WORKED EXAMPLE

Use Fig. 15 to calculate the relative atomic mass of rubidium.

Solution

1. Measure the height of each peak. The height is proportional to the amount of each isotope present.

    Height of rubidium-85 peak = 5.82 cm
    Height of rubidium-87 peak = 2.25 cm

    Therefore, the relative amounts of ^{85}Rb and ^{87}Rb are 5.82 and 2.25, respectively.

2. Express each relative amount as a percentage of the total amount. This gives the percentage abundance.

$$\% \text{ abundance} = \frac{\text{amount of isotope}}{\text{total amount of all isotopes}} \times 100$$

$$\text{\% abundance of } ^{85}\text{Rb} = \frac{5.82}{5.82 + 2.25} \times 100 = 72.1\%$$

$$\text{\% abundance of } ^{87}\text{Rb} = \frac{2.25}{5.82 + 2.25} \times 100 = 27.9\%$$

The percentage abundance figures mean that for every 100 atoms, about 72 are the ^{85}Rb isotope and about 28 are the ^{87}Rb isotope.

3. Find the total mass of an average sample of 100 atoms.

$$\text{Total mass} = \left((85 \times 72.1) + (87 \times 27.9) \right) \text{amu}$$

$$= (6129 + 2427) \text{ amu} = 8556 \text{ amu}$$

$$= 8.56 \times 10^3 \text{ amu (3 sig. figs)}$$

4. Find the average mass. This gives the relative atomic mass of rubidium.

$$\text{Average mass} = \frac{\text{total mass}}{\text{number of atoms}} = \frac{8.56 \times 10^3 \text{ amu}}{100} = 85.6 \text{ amu}$$

$$\therefore \text{ relative atomic mass } = 85.6$$

The letters amu represent atomic mass unit; 1 amu $= 1.660 \times 10^{-27}$ kg. This value was chosen because it is exactly one twelfth the mass of an atom of the carbon-12 isotope, which constitutes 98.89% of natural carbon.

Now try a similar calculation for yourself by doing the next exercise.

EXERCISE 45

Answers on page 125

Use the mass spectrum shown in Fig. 16 to calculate:
 a the percentage of each isotope present in a sample of naturally occurring lithium;
 b the relative atomic mass of lithium.

Figure 16

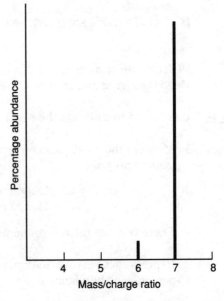

The next exercise is similar, but you are given data rather than a diagram of a mass spectrum.

EXERCISE 46

Answers on page 125

The mass spectrum of neon consists of three lines corresponding to mass/charge ratios of 20, 21 and 22 with relative intensities of 0.910, 0.0026 and 0.088, respectively. Explain the significance of these data and, hence, calculate the relative atomic mass of neon.

You could also be asked to do the reverse of this type of problem – sketch a spectrum from percentage abundance data. Have a try at this by doing the next exercise.

EXERCISE 47

Answers on page 126

a Look up the percentage abundances of the stable isotopes of chromium.
b Sketch the mass spectrum that would be obtained from naturally occurring chromium. (Let 10.0 cm represent 100% on the vertical scale.)
c Calculate the relative atomic mass of chromium, correct to three significant figures.
d Label each peak on the mass spectrum using isotopic symbols.

The relative abundances of different isotopes explain some anomalies that appear in the Periodic Table. Find out about them by doing the next exercise.

EXERCISE 48

Answers on page 126

When Mendeleev first devised the periodic table, he arranged elements in order of increasing **relative atomic mass**. In the modern version, elements are arranged in order of increasing **atomic number**.

a What would be the effect on the positions of
   i) tellurium and iodine,
   ii) argon and potassium,
   if Mendeleev's system were reintroduced?
b How do you account for this effect? (Look up the relative abundances of the isotopes of $_{52}$Te and $_{53}$I; $_{18}$Ar and $_{19}$K.)

Now try the final exercise in this section, which concerns a molecular element.

EXERCISE 49

Answers on page 126

Figure 17

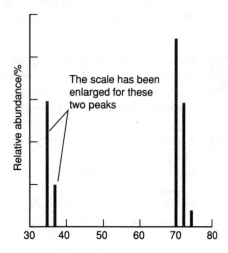

The element chlorine has isotopes of mass number 35 and 37 in the approximate proportion 3:1. Interpret the mass spectrum of gaseous chlorine shown in Fig. 17, indicating the formula (including mass number) and charge of the ion responsible for each peak.

The main use of mass spectrometry today is in identifying and analysing organic molecules which split up to give a great many different ions. We consider this aspect later in the course in one of the units on organic chemistry.

Having established that most elements have several stable isotopes, we now go on to consider some unstable isotopes which split up spontaneously releasing energy in the form of various types of radiation.

10 RADIOCHEMISTRY

CHAPTER

Radiochemistry is the study of reactions involving changes in the nucleus which result in the emission of radiation (radioactivity). Many nuclei are unstable and disintegrate spontaneously, especially those of high atomic number; all known isotopes of elements where Z is equal to or greater than 83 are radioactive. In addition, there are radioactive isotopes of many lighter elements, and here the stability depends on the relative numbers of protons and neutrons.

We now consider the different types of radioactivity.

■ 10.1 Types of radiation

Figure 18

You have probably seen the hazard warning sign for radioactive substances in a laboratory at school or college or in a hospital or factory. The danger lies in the fact that our bodies cannot detect radiation from a nucleus even though it can penetrate our bodies and damage their cells. Here we consider three types of radiation which can be emitted by nuclei of radioactive isotopes (radioisotopes).

OBJECTIVES When you have finished this section you should be able to:
- describe the properties of **alpha (α), beta (β)** and **gamma (γ) radiation** in terms of charge, mass and behaviour in a magnetic field;
- state the relative penetrating powers of alpha, beta and gamma radiation.

Read about the three types of **radioactivity** and their properties, listed in the Objectives, so that you can do the following exercises. Note that although the distinction between radiation and particles is rather an arbitrary one, as you will see later, we usually regard γ radiation as an electromagnetic wave, and α and β emissions as particles.

EXERCISE 50
Answers on page 126

Figure 19 shows how α and β particles and γ rays, emitted from a radioactive source, S, behave in an electric field.
a Use the information on the diagram to identify the type of emission present at P, Q and R.
b By what other means could a similar pattern of deflection of the three types of radiation be caused?

Figure 19

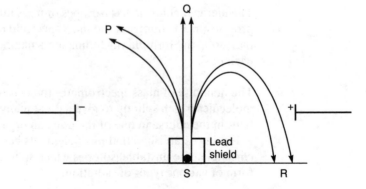

EXERCISE 51
Answers on page 127

Copy and complete the following table to summarise the properties of α, β and γ emissions.

Table 5

Emission	Nature	Relative mass and charge	Symbol	Extent of deflection in electric or magnetic field	Relative penetration
Alpha, α					
Beta, β					
Gamma, γ					

It is important for you to realise that the electrons in β emission come from the nucleus. You consider this point in the next exercise.

EXERCISE 52
Answers on page 127

A nucleus consists of protons and neutrons and yet, during β decay, it gives off electrons. Using isotopic symbols, write an equation to show how this is possible.

In the next section you apply your knowledge of α and β particles to writing nuclear equations.

■ 10.2 Nuclear reactions

Whereas chemical reactions leave the nucleus untouched and involve only the electrons surrounding it, nuclear reactions rearrange the particles within the nucleus. Also, different elements may be formed, in a process known as transmutation, which does not, of course, occur in ordinary chemical reactions.

   We now examine some nuclear reactions and show you how to write equations for them.

OBJECTIVE

When you have finished this section you should be able to:
■ complete and balance simple **nuclear equations**.

The basic nuclear reactions are α- and β-particle emission, often called α and β decay. We go through the α decay in detail in the next Worked Example. Read through it and then do the exercise which follows.

WORKED EXAMPLE

When thorium-228 decays, each atom emits one α particle. Write a balanced nuclear equation to show the process.

Solution

1. Write out the equation, putting in letters for the unknowns:

$$^{228}_{90}\text{Th} \rightarrow {}^{4}_{2}\text{He} + {}^{A}_{Z}\text{X}$$

In these equations, the atomic numbers and mass numbers of each side must balance; this allows you to calculate the unknowns, A and Z and X.

2. Find the atomic number of the new element, X, using the atomic numbers shown in the equation.

$$_{90}\text{Th} \rightarrow {}_{2}\text{He} + {}_{Z}\text{X}$$

$$90 = 2 + Z$$

$$Z = 90 - 2 = 88$$

3. Use a Periodic Table to identify the new element:
   element with atomic number 88 is radium

$$\therefore X = Ra$$

4. Find the mass number of the particular isotope of radium, using the mass numbers in the equation.

$$^{228}Th \rightarrow {}^4He + {}^AX$$

$$228 = 4 + A$$

$$\therefore A = 224$$

5. Write out the complete equation:

$$^{228}_{90}Th \rightarrow {}^4_2He + {}^{224}_{88}X$$

Note that ionic charges are not shown in nuclear equations. You may wonder, for example, why we do not write

$$^4_2He^{2+}$$

In fact, the positive ions tend to pick up stray electrons and so the charges are usually omitted as a simplification. This also focuses attention on changes in the nucleus.

Now try some calculations yourself, by doing the next exercise.

EXERCISE 53
Answers on page 127

Write balanced nuclear equations to show the α decay of:

a $^{212}_{84}Po$,

b $^{220}_{86}Rn$.

You can adapt the method given in the last Worked Example to write an equation for β decay.

You may need to remind yourself of how the process takes place (see your answers to Exercises 51 and 52); then go on to try the next exercise.

EXERCISE 54
Answers on page 127

Write balanced nuclear equations to show the β decay of:

a $^{212}_{84}Po$,

b $^{24}_{11}Na$,

c $^{108}_{47}Ag$.

For further practice in writing nuclear equations, try the next exercise.

EXERCISE 55
Answers on page 127

Write the nuclear equations which represent:

a the loss of an α particle by radium-226,
b the loss of a β particle by potassium-43,
c the loss of an α particle by the product of **b**.

Finally, to summarise your knowledge of the effects of α and β decay on the nucleus, do the next exercise.

EXERCISE 56

Answers on page 127

What happens to the atomic number and the mass number of a nucleus when it emits:

a an α particle,

b a β particle.

The decay of a single unstable nucleus is instantaneous and we cannot say when it will happen. However, we can measure the rate of decomposition (decay) of a sample containing many nuclei by counting the number of disintegrations which occur in unit time. In the next chapter, we look at the way in which the rate of decay varies with time.

CHAPTER 11

THE RATE OF DECAY OF RADIOISOTOPES

The rate at which a particular radioactive isotope decays depends only on the amount present – it is unaffected by external factors such as temperature or pressure. In this chapter, we introduce the idea of half-life. This provides both a way to compare the rates of decay of different isotopes and, since no two isotopes have exactly the same half-life, a method of identification.

■ 11.1 Half-life

OBJECTIVE   When you have finished this section you should be able to:
■ define the term **half-life**.

   Read about half-life in your textbook. The term is used in connection with other reactions too, but you should concentrate on references to **radioactive decay**. We suggest that you don't worry about a mathematical treatment at this stage – look for a graphical description. This should be sufficient to help you do the next two exercises.

EXERCISE 57
Answers on page 127

a Define the term 'half-life' as applied to a radioactive isotope.
b Why is it meaningless to speak of the 'total life' of a radioactive isotope?

EXERCISE 58
Answers on page 128

a Use the data in Table 6 to plot a decay curve for the transuranium element americium-239.

Table 6

Mass of sample/mg	Time/h
0.512	0
0.256	12
0.128	24
0.064	36
0.032	48
0.016	60
0.008	72
0.004	84
0.002	96
0.001	108
0.0005	120

Plot mass of sample on the vertical axis and time on the horizontal axis.
b What happens to the rate of a radioactive decay reaction, like this one, as it proceeds?
c How long would it take for the mass of americium to reach zero?
d Describe the shape that the curve would have if we had asked you to plot activity, in counts min^{-1}, rather than mass of sample.
e What percentage of the original activity remains after ten half-lives?

We now go on to consider an important application of the half-life of radioisotopes, radioactive dating.

■ 11.2 Radioactive dating

Half-lives of certain radioactive elements have been used to calculate the age of rocks and estimate the age of the earth. In this section, we examine the use of carbon-14 in the dating of archaeological remains.

OBJECTIVE   When you have finished this section you should be able to:
■ explain the use of the $^{14}_{6}$C isotope in **radiocarbon dating**.

Read about radiocarbon dating in your textbook. Find out why the amount of $^{14}_{6}$C in the atmosphere is constant and how archaeologists use this to find the age of objects from the past. We suggest that you do not concern yourself too much with the mathematical aspects at this stage, but you should be able to do simple calculations based directly on the concept of half-life, as in the next exercise.

EXERCISE 59   **a** Complete the following nuclear equation which shows how carbon-14 is formed from
Answers on page 129   nitrogen-14 by the action of cosmic radiation:

$$^{14}_{7}\text{N} + ^{1}_{0}\text{n} \rightarrow ^{14}_{6}\text{C} + ^{A}_{Z}\text{X}$$

b Carbon from a piece of wood from a beam found in an ancient tomb gave a reading of 7.5 counts per minute per gram. New wood gives a reading of 15 counts per minute per gram. Estimate the year in which the tomb was built given that the half-life of $^{14}_{6}$C is 5730 years.

c What is assumed to be constant over the period?

We have already mentioned one use of radioisotopes, in dating objects from the past. In this final section on radiochemistry, we suggest some reading on the many other uses of radioisotopes.

■ 11.3 Uses of radioisotopes

OBJECTIVE   When you have finished this section you should be able to:
■ state at least four ways in which **radioisotopes** are used and explain the principle behind each use.

Most textbooks have a section covering the uses of radioisotopes. Look through a few books until you find one that gives a fairly detailed treatment. Among the uses to look out for are:

■ atomic bombs
■ nuclear reactors
■ radiotherapy
■ radiocarbon dating
■ tracer techniques in biology and medicine
■ thickness measurement

Figure 20
Using thalium-170 to check for defects in tube to tube sheet welds.

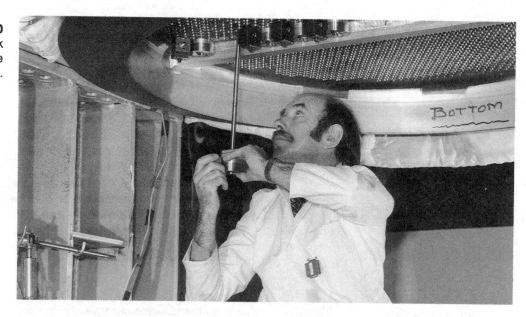

When you have read about the uses to which radioactive isotopes are being put, answer the following Teacher-marked Exercise (for advice on these, see the notes in the Introduction to the Student section at the beginning of the volume).

EXERCISE
Teacher-marked

Choose three ways in which radioisotopes are used today. For each one, explain the underlying principle.

■ Part A test

To find out how well you have learned the material in Part A, try the test which follows. Read the notes below before starting.

■ You should spend about 60 minutes on this test.
■ Hand your answers to your teacher for marking.

Questions 1–4 are either questions or incomplete statements followed by five suggested answers. Select the best answer in each case.

Figure 21

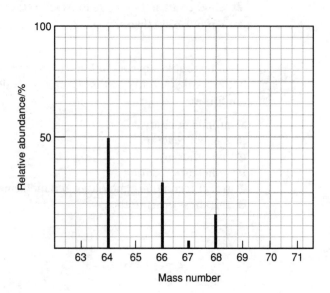

1. The graph in Fig. 21 shows the relative abundances of four isotopes of a certain element. Its relative atomic mass will be (to the nearest whole number)
   a 64,
   b 65,
   c 66,
   d 67,
   e 68. (1)

2. The isotopic composition of a certain element X is 80.00% ^{24}X, 10.00% ^{25}X and 10.00% ^{26}X. The relative atomic mass of X is
   a 25.00,
   b 24.67,
   c 24.33,
   d 24.30,
   e 24.25. (1)

3. Archaeologists can determine the age of organic matter by measuring the proportion of $^{14}_{6}$C present. Assuming that carbon-14 has a half-life of 5600 years, a piece of wood found to contain $^1/_8$ as much carbon-14 as living material is calculated to have an age, in years, of
   a 44 800,
   b 16 800,
   c 2800,
   d 1400,
   e 700. (1)

4. The nucleus of $^{23}_{11}$Na contains
   a 23 protons and 11 electrons,
   b 23 protons and 11 neutrons,
   c 11 protons and 12 neutrons,
   d 11 protons and 12 electrons,
   e 12 neutrons and 11 electrons. (1)

Directions For questions 5 and 6 **one** or **more** of the responses are correct. Decide which of the responses is (are) correct. Then choose:
   A if **1, 2** and **3** are all correct,
   B if **1** and **2** only are correct,
   C if **2** and **3** only are correct,
   D if **1** only is correct,
   E if **3** only is correct.

Directions summarised				
A	B	C	D	E
1, 2, 3	**1, 2**	**2, 3**	**1**	**3**
correct	only	only	only	only

5. In the natural state the element M consists of the isotopes $^{28}_{14}$M, $^{29}_{14}$M, $^{30}_{14}$M in the ratio 60:3:2, respectively. Correct statements about M in its natural state include that
   1 the relative atomic mass is between 28.0 and 28.5,
   2 atoms of M each contain 14 electrons,
   3 atoms of M may contain 14, 15 or 16 neutrons. (1)

6. A sample of an isotope of lead, $^{209}_{82}$Pb, has a half-life of three hours and it decays by emitting a beta particle to form a stable nuclide, X. Which of the following statements is (are) true?
   1 X has an atomic number of 81.
   2 After 6 hours 75% of the lead isotope has decayed.
   3 X has a mass number of 209. (1)

7. a Copy Table 7 and complete it by inserting properties of the three types of radioactivity.

Table 7

	Relative charge	Relative mass
α		
β		
γ		

(3)

   b Which of the types of radioactive emission has the greatest penetrating power, and which has the least? (2)

8. a Explain what is meant by each of the following terms:
   i)   electron,
   ii) proton,
   iii) neutron,
   iv) isotopes. (4)
   b The atomic number provides three pieces of information about an element. What are they? (3)
   c The radioactive atom $^{224}_{88}$Ra decays by α-emission with a half-life of 3.64 days.
   i)   What is meant by 'half-life' of 3.64 days?
   ii) Referring to the product of the decay, what will be its mass number and its atomic number?
   iii) Radium is in group II of the Periodic Table. In what group will the decay product be? (4)
   d Explain briefly the principles underlying
   i)   the use of radioactive isotopes as 'tracers',
   ii) the dating of dead organic matter using radiocarbon, $^{14}_{6}$C. (6)

9. a Explain what you understand by the terms:
   i)   mass number,
   ii) relative atomic mass. (2)
   b Calculate the relative atomic mass of copper assuming it to contain 70% of ^{63}Cu and 30% of ^{65}Cu. (2)
   c Briefly explain the principles of the use of the mass spectrometer for determining the mass number. (6)
   d Complete the following equations:

   $$^{220}_{86}Rn \rightarrow ^{216}_{84}Po +$$

   $$^{214}_{82}Pb \rightarrow ^{214}_{83}Bi +$$

   (4)

   e The activity of a sample of $^{222}_{86}$Rn is reduced to 25% of its initial value after eight days. What is the half-life of $^{226}_{86}$Rn? (2)

10. The mass spectrum of an element enables the relative abundance of each isotope of the element to be determined. Data relating to the mass spectrum of bromine, atomic number 35, appear below.

Mass number of isotope	79	81
% Relative abundance	50.5	49.5

  a Define the term 'isotope'. (2)

  b Write down the conventional symbols for the two isotopes of bromine. (1)

  c Calculate the relative atomic mass of bromine to three significant figures. (2)

  d i) Make a copy of Fig. 22 and on it sketch the expected spectrum of bromine vapour in the *m/e* region shown.

    ii) Explain the origin of each peak in your spectrum. (5)

Figure 22

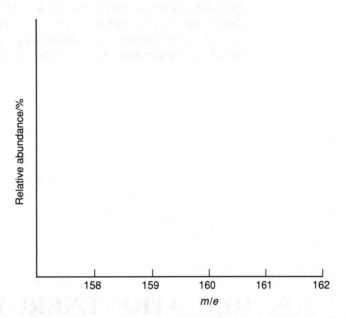

The isotopes of some elements emit radiation, characterised by a particular half-life. For example, ^{24}Na is a beta emitter having a half-life of 15.0 hours.

  e i) Name two other types of radiation which may be emitted by radioisotopes.

    ii) Which of these has the greater penetrating power?

    iii) What is meant by the term 'half-life'?

    iv) A patient receives a dose of sodium chloride containing ^{24}Na, giving a reading of 1200 counts s^{-1} in a blood sample. How many hours must pass for the reading of this sample to fall to 75 counts s^{-1}? (6)

(Total: 60 marks)

PART B

ELECTRON ARRANGEMENTS

Having considered the nucleus in Part A, we now move on to the electrons. We cannot 'see' electrons in a physical sense and yet chemistry is based on a description of where they are in an atom and how they move. Information about the arrangement of electrons has been obtained by 'disturbing' them, in two ways:

a by bombarding them with streams of fast-moving particles and so detaching them from the atom;

b by forcing them into higher energy states and observing what happens when they return to normal.

Method **a** allows us to measure approximately the energy required to detach an electron, called the ionisation energy; method **b** is the basis of emission spectroscopy and provides a better way of measuring ionisation energies.

The study of ionisation energies helps us to understand how electrons are arranged around the nucleus and how they behave in chemical reactions.

CHAPTER 12

IONISATION ENERGY

It would be more accurate to name this term 'ionisation enthalpy' but to avoid confusion we shall use 'ionisation energy', as is done in most textbooks.

In your study of the mass spectrometer, you saw in Part A how atoms lose electrons to become positively charged ions. In this chapter we consider the energy change needed to bring about the process.

12.1 First and successive ionisation energies

OBJECTIVES   When you have finished this section you should be able to:
■ define **first ionisation energy**;
■ write equations representing first, second, third and subsequent ionisation energies of a given element.

Read the section on ionisation energy in your textbook. Look in detail at the definition of first ionisation energy, bearing in mind that it refers to atoms in the gaseous state, then try the next exercise.

EXERCISE 60

Answers on page 129

a Define the term first ionisation energy.
b Write an equation to show the first ionisation of sodium.
c Use your data book to find a value for the first ionisation energy of sodium.

Note: Ionisation energies are usually quoted in kJ mol^{-1}. However, in some books (mostly older ones) you may find the term 'electron-volt' (eV), which is not a proper unit at all but is the product of a physical quantity (e) and a unit (V) (and is certainly not an SI unit!).

The charge on an electron is 1.6021×10^{-19} C

$\therefore$ 1 electron accelerated by 1 volt gains 1.6021×10^{-19} J

There are 6.0225×10^{23} electrons in 1 mole of electrons

$\therefore$ 1 mole of electrons accelerated by 1 volt gains

$1.6021 \times 10^{-19} \times 6.0225 \times 10^{23}$ J = 96 486 J

$$1 \text{ eV} \equiv 96.5 \text{ kJ mol}^{-1}$$

Now read about successive ionisation energies.

The important point about ionisation energies after the first one is that an electron is removed from a positively charged ion each time. To make sure you understand this idea, try the next exercise.

EXERCISE 61

Answers on page 129

a Write equations to show the first, second and third ionisation energies of aluminium.
b Would you expect the values of these ionisation energies to increase or decrease in the order first, second, third?
c Explain your answer to **b**.

Now we go on to consider how successive ionisation energies give information about the arrangement of electrons.

■ 12.2 Ionisation energies and the arrangement of electrons

In this section you use successive ionisation energy values for a specific element and find that they provide evidence for the arrangement of electrons around the nucleus.

OBJECTIVES

When you have finished this section you should be able to:
- ■ deduce the **electron arrangement** of an element from a graph of $\log_{10}$ ionisation energy against number of electron removed;
- ■ use a graph of **successive ionisation energy** against number of electron removed to provide evidence for the existence of sub-shells.

In the next two exercises, you examine successive ionisation energy data for calcium and draw conclusions about its electron arrangement.

EXERCISE 62

Answers on page 129

a For the element calcium, plot $\log_{10}$ (I.E.) against the number (one, two, three, ...) of the electron removed using the data in Table 8.

Table 8

No. of electron removed	Ionisation energy (I.E.) /kJ mol^{-1}	Log$_{10}$ (I.E./kJ mol^{-1})
1	590	2.77
2	1145	3.06
3	4912	3.69
4	6474	3.81
5	8145	3.91
6	10496	4.02
7	12320	4.09
8	14207	4.15
9	18192	4.26
10	20385	4.31
11	57048	4.76
12	63333	4.80
13	70052	4.85
14	78792	4.90
15	86367	4.94
16	94000	4.97
17	104900	5.02
18	111600	5.05
19	494790	5.69
20	527759	5.72

b What information does this graph give about the electron configuration of the calcium atom?

c Why were you asked to plot $\log_{10}$ (I.E.) and not just ionisation energy?

d Explain why the ionisation energy increases when electrons are successively removed from a given shell.

This exercise fits the Bohr planetary model of the atom with which you are familiar. The large jumps in the value of the ionisation energy indicate shells of different energies. You probably used a diagram like one of those shown in Fig. 23 to represent the structure of the calcium atom.

Figure 23

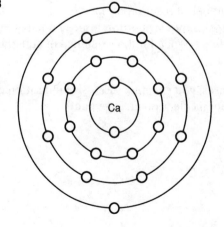
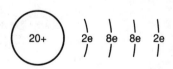

However, we now take a closer look at the ionisation energies of electrons in a given shell, and find that this picture is oversimplified. There is evidence for a structure within each shell. To find out what this is, go on to do the next exercise.

EXERCISE 63

Answers on page 130

a From the data given in Exercise 62 plot a graph of ionisation energy [not $\log_{10}$ (I.E.)] against the number of electrons removed for electrons 3 to 10.
   (Let 1 cm = 1000 kJ mol^{-1} on the vertical axis and 1 cm = 1 electron on the horizontal axis.)

b In the previous exercise, you learned that large jumps in ionisation energy represent electrons being removed from different energy shells. What is your conclusion about the small jump which occurs between the eighth and ninth electrons?

c In view of your answer to **b**, suggest how electrons are arranged in the second shell.

This exercise has shown you the shortcomings of the Bohr planetary model of the atom. But does this mean that the Bohr model is completely useless? In the next chapter we pause to consider models in general, before going on to discuss a more sophisticated picture of the atom.

13 MODELS AND THEIR USEFULNESS

You are probably more familiar with the term 'model' to describe a scaled-down version of an everyday object, such as a model car. But model cars differ enormously in the accuracy and detail with which the original is reproduced. At one extreme is the miniature replica, identical in every feature, including an engine, which burns fuel and moves the car along. Less refined is the familiar 'Dinky toy' model, which is recognisable in many details as a particular make of car, but has no working parts. Even less refined is the sort of model an architect might use for a new town centre plan – a solid, car-shaped block, to give an impression of the relative sizes of road and car. Finally, at the other extreme, there is the model a motorist would use after a car accident – just a rectangle on a map to indicate where the vehicle was at the time of impact.

None of these models is strictly 'correct' but each has its own use in a given situation. In a similar way, there are several models of the atom – from the solid sphere of John Dalton to the planetary model of Rutherford and Bohr with electrons as particles circling a central nucleus in fixed orbits (see Fig. 24).

Figure 24
(a) The solar system.
(b) Planetary model of the atom.

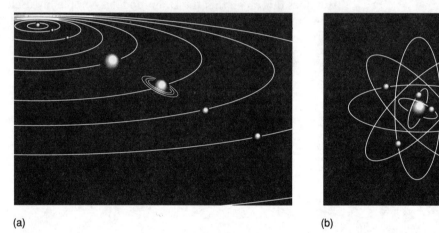

(a)   (b)

A further model, the orbital model, which we are going to use in the rest of this unit, treats electrons as waves.

As we move more deeply into the subject, we meet increasingly detailed and sophisticated descriptions of atomic structure. But must we therefore discard earlier descriptions as 'wrong' and useless? In fact, there is no need to do so. For many purposes, such as explaining the states of matter, there is no point in using anything more complicated than the simple 'billiard ball' picture; in other cases, the planetary model is all that is needed. At A-level you will continue to use the simple electron shell model, for example, to explain ionic compound formation.

Scientific theories are rather like models: they can be simple or elaborate, depending on the job they have to do. It is usually more sensible to ask not whether a model is 'right' but whether it is useful. This is an important underlying theme in chemistry (and in science generally) and we shall return to it from time to time.

Before considering the orbital model of the atom as such, we spend a short time on the nature of electrons.

■ 13.1 Wave–particle duality

Until now, it has been convenient to think of electrons as minute, almost massless particles, but there is evidence to suggest that they also behave as waves.

OBJECTIVE When you have finished this section you should be able to:
■ describe briefly what is meant by the **wave–particle duality** of an electron.

Electron beams can behave like beams of light. For example, they can be diffracted, and diffraction is a property of **waves**. Read about the evidence which shows that electrons can behave as waves. Try '**electron diffraction**' or '**electron, wave nature**' in the index of you textbook(s).

Figure 25(a) shows an electron diffraction pattern obtained by passing a beam of electrons through aluminium foil. Notice the similarity to Fig. 25(b), which is the pattern obtained by passing X-rays through aluminium foil.

Figure 25 Diffraction patterns for aluminium produced by electrons (left) and X-rays (right).

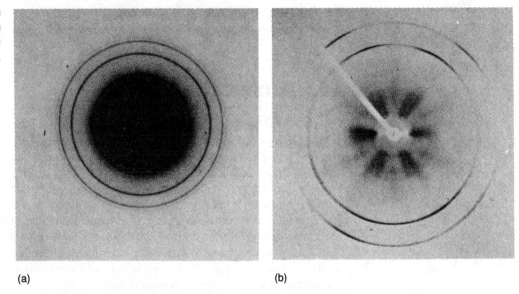

(a)   (b)

Clearly, then, we need more than one model for the electron. To explain some properties, we regard electrons as particles; to explain others, we regard them as waves. In other words, they appear to have a dual nature. This phenomenon is known as 'wave–particle duality'.

It was by treating electrons as waves and applying to them mathematical methods, known as wave mechanics, that scientists came up with pictures of electron distribution. We go on to consider this model, where electrons do not occupy fixed orbits as in the planetary model, but orbitals, which describe how their charges are spread out in small regions of space.

14 THE ORBITAL MODEL OF AN ATOM

The main distinction between the planetary and orbital models of the atom is that while the planetary model assumes that electrons keep to fixed orbits around the nucleus, the orbital model is based on the **probability** of finding an electron in a certain volume of space.

OBJECTIVES When you have finished this chapter you should be able to:
- give a simple, non-mathematical description of an **orbital** in terms of probabilities;
- draw the shapes of an **s-orbital** and a **p-orbital**;
- state the maximum number of electrons that an orbital can hold.

■ 14.1 Atomic orbitals

Look up 'orbitals' in a textbook and read the section on **atomic orbitals**. At this stage, ignore references to other sorts of orbital, such as molecular, metallic, bonding and anti-bonding orbitals. You need not worry about a mathematical treatment of orbitals.

An important point to bear in mind as you do your reading is the close relationship between the energy of an electron and its distance from the nucleus. As you saw from the successive ionisation energy data, the further an electron is from the nucleus, the less energy is needed to strip it away from the atom. Outer electrons are at higher energy levels, less strongly attracted by the charge on the nucleus and, therefore, easier to remove.

In your reading, you may also come across the phrase 'quantum shell' used for energy shell. It arises from quantum theory which, when applied to electrons in atoms, says that the electron can only exist in certain definite energy states. These energy states are called quantum shells.

As an extra help in picturing an orbital, we now include a short analogy. Read through this before attempting the exercise which follows.

Imagine that you were able to take a large number of **photographs** of a hydrogen atom (which you are not), containing one electron. By superimposing these photographs, you would obtain an impression of where the electron spends most of its time. The picture you would get would be something like Fig. 26.

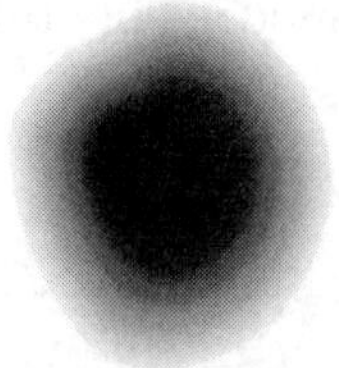

Figure 26
Hydrogen atom 'charge cloud'.

The picture is itself an oversimplification since it is restricted to two dimensions. The complete model is three-dimensional and spherical. Since even the two-dimensional picture is tedious to draw, we often use instead a boundary round the region where the probability of finding an electron is high – about 98% – as shown in Fig. 27. The space enclosed by this boundary is often called a probability envelope, or an orbital. At a more advanced level, you may have to make a mathematical distinction between probability envelopes and orbitals, but we shall regard them as the same, in common with most A-level textbooks.

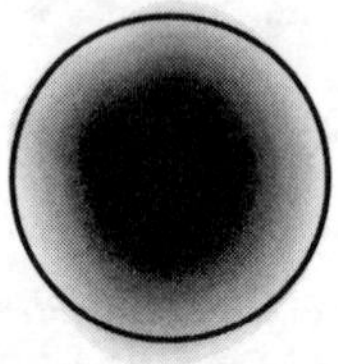

Figure 27
Orbital boundary superimposed on charge cloud.

EXERCISE 64
Answers on page 130

In the planetary model of the atom, we say that the electron follows a definite path in space. How does the orbital model differ from this?

■ 14.2 How many electrons per orbital?

In case you did not answer this question in your reading, we suggest you work it out for yourself, by doing the next exercise.

EXERCISE 65
Answers on page 130

The number of orbitals in a quantum shell is given by n^2, where n is the number of the shell. Use your knowledge of the total number of electrons in a shell to work out how many electrons a single orbital can hold.

Not all orbitals are spherical like the one shown in Fig. 27. In the next section, we look at some other shapes as well.

■ 14.3 The shapes of orbitals

There are four types of orbitals whose shapes have been worked out, using wave mechanics. They are referred to by letter: s, p, d and f. These are the initial letters of the words 'sharp', 'principal', 'diffuse' and 'fundamental', originating from work carried out on the hydrogen spectrum which led to our present-day view of shells and sub-shells. You need only remember the initial letter.

You should be familiar with the shapes of s- and p-orbitals and we include d-orbitals for interest, but f-orbitals are too complex to show on a two-dimensional page.

Figure 28
The shape of s-, p- and d-orbitals.

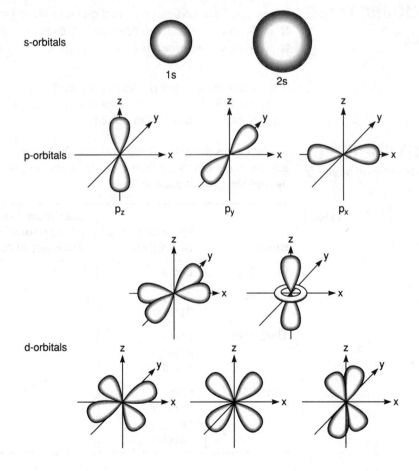

Study Fig. 28 which shows the shapes of s-, p- and d-orbitals as predicted by wave mechanical calculations. Note that the shading or 'dotting' in these diagrams is not intended to represent electron density but is merely to provide a three-dimensional effect. You should also return to the section on orbitals in your textbook and read descriptions of these shapes. Then do the next two exercises.

EXERCISE 66
Answers on page 131

Explain why p-orbitals are labelled 'p_x', 'p_y' and 'p_z'. (d-Orbitals are also given labels, but as they are not straightforward we have omitted them.)

EXERCISE 67
Answers on page 131

a How many electrons can be held in
  i) an s-orbital,
  ii) a set of three p-orbitals?
b Use one word in each case to describe the shape of
  i) an s-orbital,
  ii) a p-orbital.

In the next section, we go on to consider how many orbitals of each type there are in each electron shell.

■ 14.4 The number and types of orbitals in an electron shell

Each shell has a certain number of orbitals associated with it. In this section, we list these and you calculate the total number of electrons in a shell.

OBJECTIVES

When you have finished this section you should be able to:
■ state which orbitals are present in the first four **electron shells**;
■ write down the order in which orbitals are filled in the first four electron shells.

The maximum number of electrons a shell can contain is given by $2n^2$, where n is the number of the shell. Use this expression in the exercise which follows to work out the total number of electrons in a shell.

EXERCISE 68
Answers on page 131

Table 9 gives the orbitals associated with the first four electron shells. Copy the table and fill in the last two columns to check the sum of the electrons in the separate orbitals against the total in each shell.

Table 9

Shell	No. and types of orbitals	Maximum number of electrons in each set of orbitals	Maximum number of electrons in the shell
First shell	one s		
Second shell	one s three p		
Third shell	one s three p five d		
Fourth shell	one s three p five d seven f		

In the next section, we go on to consider the order in which orbitals are filled. First you need to know something about their different energy levels. Figure 29 shows the orbitals in the first four shells for a typical light element, as well as some orbitals from the fifth to seventh shells. Each orbital is represented by a square box, □. The vertical axis represents energy of the atom and is roughly to scale. Note, however, that the energies vary from element to element, and even the order of energy levels may be different for heavier elements (see ILPAC Volume 11, Transition Elements).

Study Fig. 29 and then do the exercise which follows.

Figure 29

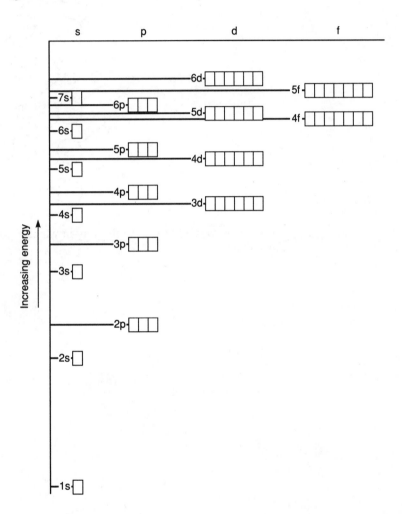

EXERCISE 69

Answer on page 131

Use Fig. 29 to list the first ten sub-shells in order of increasing energy.

In an atom, the orbitals are filled in order of increasing energy starting from 1s.
An aid to remembering this order is to write down the orbitals in columns, as shown below.

7s	7p		
6s	6p	6d	
5s	5p	5d	5f
4s	4p	4d	4f
3s	3p	3d	
2s	2p		
1s			

The order is then given by drawing diagonal lines through the symbols, as in Fig. 30.

Figure 30

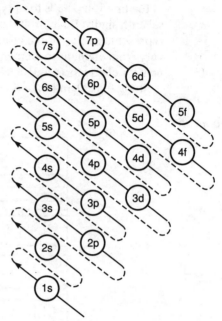

You are now ready to study the way in which electrons fill the available orbitals in an atom.

15

THE ARRANGEMENT OF ELECTRONS IN THEIR ORBITALS

We shall start with hydrogen, the simplest element, which has a single electron in the lowest energy orbital, the 1s. Then we go through the elements in order of increasing atomic number, imagining the addition of an extra electron each time. This process is known as the aufbau or 'building-up' principle [aufbau is a German word meaning to build up, pronounced 'owf-bow' (as in 'bow-wow')]. As you go through it, the pattern of the Periodic Table emerges and we draw this together at the end of the chapter. We also introduce the conventional ways of writing out electron configurations.

OBJECTIVES

When you have finished this chapter you should be able to:

■ use the **aufbau principle** to work out the order in which orbitals are filled in a given element;
■ express **electronic configurations** using
  a the **electrons-in-boxes** method;
  b the **s, p, d, f** notation;
■ write down the electronic configuration of any element or ion in the first four periods of the Periodic Table.

■ 15.1 The aufbau principle

We now state three important rules which determine the order in which electrons occupy the vacant orbitals in an atom.

1. Of the available orbitals, the added electron will always occupy the one at the lowest energy level.
2. Each orbital may hold only two electrons, and they must have opposite spin.* (Pauli exclusion principle.)
3. Where a number of orbitals at equal energy level are available, the added electron will go into an empty orbital, keeping electron spins the same, before spin-pairing occurs. (Hund's rule.)

As an example of how Hund's rule operates, consider two electrons entering the p-orbital. There seem to be three possible arrangements

but the first is the only one which conforms to Hund's rule.

As an analogy, think of a double-decker bus in which passengers fill up the lower deck before climbing upstairs and in which, given the choice, passengers prefer to sit alone rather than share the seats.

We now apply the rules and work through the elements from hydrogen according to the aufbau principle.

Hydrogen The hydrogen atom contains one electron which therefore occupies the lowest energy orbital – the 1s orbital. The electron configuration is represented by:

*Electrons can be thought of as spinning on an axis like the earth. Unlike the earth, however, which spins in only one direction, an electron can spin in either of two directions. The ↑ arrow represents one direction of spin; the ↓ arrow the other. Furthermore, in any one 'box' when there are two electrons occupying it, they will spin in opposite directions. This is called spin-pairing and is shown as ↑↓.

Helium The helium atom contains two electrons. Since the 1s orbital still has room for another electron, the second electron goes into it, and the configuration is:

1s

Lithium The lithium atom contains two 1s electrons and the third electron goes into the next orbital, i.e. the 2s orbital. Hence the electron configuration is:

2s

1s

Notice that we always label the boxes. By now you should be able to work out what happens for the next four elements.

EXERCISE 70
Answers on page 131

Draw the electron configuration of beryllium.

EXERCISE 71
Answers on page 131

Make three copies of part of Fig. 29 as shown, and draw in arrows to show the electron configurations of:
a boron,
b carbon,
c nitrogen.

You can save time and space in writing down electron configurations by placing the orbital boxes in a row, as we now show.

■ 15.2 Boxes-in-a-row

Obviously, on paper it is difficult to get the vertical spacings between energy levels right. However, the spacings are usually not critical and the boxes are most often placed side by side. We shall refer to this arrangement as 'boxes-in-a-row', or 'electrons-in-boxes'.

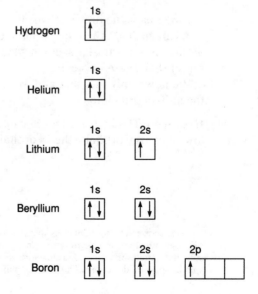

Remembering to label the boxes, do the next exercise.

EXERCISE 72

Answers on page 131

Draw boxes-in-a-row to show the electron configurations of
a carbon,
b nitrogen.

Now we look at a further simplification in writing down electron configurations.

■ 15.3 Using a noble gas 'core'

The 'boxes-in-a-row' method can become tedious, particularly if the atom contains very many electrons. In any case, we are most often concerned with the outermost electrons in an atom – the inner 'core' is not involved in chemical reactions. Consequently, we can use a symbol for a noble gas to replace some of the arrows. This is possible for both the next two elements. Notice also that from this point on, electrons entering 2p orbitals have to pair up with electrons which are already there. The electron configurations are therefore:

Oxygen (He)   2s ↑↓   2p ↑↓ ↑ ↑

and

Fluorine (He)   2s ↑↓   2p ↑↓ ↑ ↓↑

Now try this shorter method for the first two elements in the next period.

EXERCISE 73

Answers on page 132

Using boxes-in-a-row, and noble gas cores, draw diagrams to show the electron configurations of
a sodium,
b magnesium.

Another method of writing electron configurations does away with boxes altogether.

■ 15.4 The s, p, d, f notation

In this method, the electron configuration of hydrogen is represented by

One electron in this orbital

$1s^1$

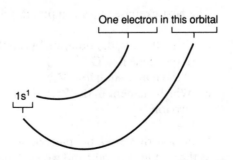

Using this notation, the next three elements in the third period are:

aluminium	$1s^2 2s^2 2p^6 3s^2 3p^1$
silicon	$1s^2 2s^2 2p^6 3s^2 3p^2$
phosphorus	$1s^2 2s^2 2p^6 3s^2 3p^3$

and, of course, the noble gas core can be used here too:

aluminium	$(Ne)3s^2 3p^1$
silicon	$(Ne)3s^2 3p^2$
phosphorus	$(Ne)3s^2 3p^3$

Now do the next exercise in which you use this notation for the last three elements in this period.

EXERCISE 74

Answers on page 132

Use the s, p, d, f notation to write the electron configurations for
a sulphur,
b chlorine,
c argon.

The electron configurations of ions derived from atoms can be represented in a similar manner. Here are three examples.

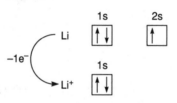

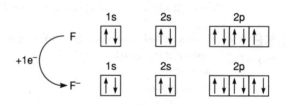

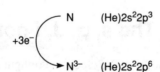

The next exercise gives you practice at writing electron configurations of ions.

EXERCISE 75

Answers on page 132

a Using the s, p, d, f notation, write the electron configurations of
   i) the oxide ion, O^{2-},
   ii) the magnesium ion, Mg^{2+}.
b Which element in the Periodic Table has the same electron configuration as these two ions?

In the fourth period, the pattern becomes more interesting. This is sometimes known as the first long period and we shall now see why. The electron configurations of the first two elements are straightforward. Work these out yourself, by doing the next exercise.

EXERCISE 76
Answers on page 132

Write the electron configurations of
a the potassium atom,
b the calcium atom, using the s, p, d, f notation.

Before you do the next exercise, look at the energy level diagram, Fig. 29. What does this tell you about the added electron in the next element, scandium?

Remember that an electron will always enter the orbital of lowest energy. Which has the lower energy – 3d or 4s?

Also, you write out the orbitals in numerical order, not the order in which they are filled. Thus, the order from the third shell is:

3s 3p 3d 4s 4p 4d 4f 5s . . . , etc.

EXERCISE 77
Answers on page 132

Write the electron configuration of scandium using the s, p, d, f notation.

Scandium, therefore, differs from calcium by having one electron in the 3d orbital. Now there are five equivalent 3d orbitals. Consequently, not just the scandium electron, but ten electrons can enter the third shell before it becomes necessary for them to go into the 4p orbital.

The series of elements:

Sc   Ti   V   Cr   Mn   Fe   Co   Ni   Cu   Zn

represents this filling-up of the d orbitals. (We will return to this in ILPAC Volume 11, Transition Elements.)

For an introduction to the electron configuration of this series of elements, try the next exercise.

EXERCISE 78
Answers on page 132

Write the electron configurations of
a the titanium atom,
b the vanadium atom,
c the iron atom.
In each case use
   i) electrons-in-boxes,
   ii) the s, p, d, f notation.

After zinc, electrons enter the 4p orbitals until, at krypton, these are full. To see how electrons fill in the rest of the fourth period, try the next exercise.

EXERCISE 79
Answers on page 132

Write the electron configurations of
a the gallium ion, Ga^+,
b the arsenic atom,
c the bromide ion.
In each case use
   i) electrons-in-boxes,
   ii) the s, p, d, f notation.

The fifth period starts with rubidium and strontium, very much like the fourth period. Then with the 5s orbital full, electrons enter the 4d orbitals until these too are full. Finally, the 5p orbitals are filled.

In the next period, the pattern changes slightly. Look again at the energy diagram, Fig. 29. Use the information in the diagram to help you do the next exercise.

EXERCISE 80
Answer on page 133

Write down the orbitals which are filled in going across the sixth period.

The seventh period of the Periodic Table is similar, but incomplete.

You can now look at the Periodic Table as a whole and explain the major blocks into which it is divided. The Periodic Table shown in Fig. 31 is the 'long form' – to see why, compare it with other versions of the table. Study the table and use it to do the exercise which follows.

Figure 31

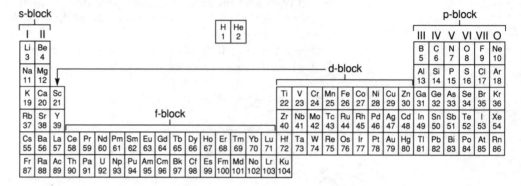

EXERCISE 81

Answers on page 133

a Explain why the s-block, p-block, d-block and f-block are so called.

b For the s- and p-block elements, the number of the last sub-shell to be occupied is the same as that of the period. Is this true of the d- and f-block elements? Give examples from periods 4, 5 and 6.

In the next chapter, we return briefly to the topic of ionisation energy.

CHAPTER **16** **FURTHER ASPECTS OF IONISATION ENERGY**

■ **16.1 Using ionisation energy values to identify an element**

At the start of Part B we used ionisation energies as evidence for the shells and sub-shells in a calcium atom. You should also be able to reverse this process to identify an element from its ionisation energy values.

OBJECTIVE When you have finished this section you should be able to:
■ identify an element, given values of **successive ionisation energies**.

The following exercise is part of an A-level question. Work through it to make sure that you can identify an element given $\log_{10}$ ionisation energy.

EXERCISE 82
Answers on page 133

Table 10 shows the logarithms of all the successive ionisation energies for a given element, X.

Table 10

Electron No.	1	2	3	4	5	6	7	8
$\log_{10}$ (I.E.)	3.12	3.53	3.72	3.88	4.04	4.12	4.85	4.92

a Plot $\log_{10}$ (I.E.) against the number (first, second, third, etc.) of the electron removed.
b Write down the electronic configuration of this element using the s, p, d, f notation.
c To which group of the Periodic Table does the element belong?
d What is the formula of its ion?

You should also be able to identify an element by inspecting the successive ionisation energy values and identifying the major 'jumps' or increases as changes of shell. The next exercise, which is part of an A-level question, gives you practice at this.

EXERCISE 83
Answers on page 133

Table 11 shows the first six ionisation energy values for each of four consecutive elements in the Periodic Table.

Table 11

Element	Ionisation energy/kJ mol^{-1}					
	First	Second	Third	Fourth	Fifth	Sixth
W	1260	2300	3800	5200	6500	9300
X	1520	2700	3900	5800	7200	8800
Y	420	3100	4400	5900	8000	9600
Z	590	1100	4900	6500	8100	10500

Which of the elements do you think
a is a noble gas,
b will form an ion with a single positive charge,
c will form an ion with a double positive charge?

At the end of the last chapter, you saw how the addition of one electron to each successive element gives rise to the Periodic Table. We now consider the pattern which emerges from the first ionisation energies of successive elements.

■ 16.2 First ionisation energies of successive elements

If the first ionisation energies of successive elements in the Periodic Table are plotted against atomic number, an interesting graph emerges.

OBJECTIVES

When you have finished this section you should be able to:
■ plot a graph of **first ionisation energy against atomic number**;
■ explain the term '**periodic**' with reference to the plot of first ionisation energy against atomic number;
■ explain the changes in first ionisation energy that take place across the second period.

EXERCISE 84

Answers on page 133

Plot a graph of first ionisation energy against atomic number for the first 20 elements (i.e. up to Ca).

Label the vertical axis: 'First ionisation energy/kJ mol^{-1}', and extend the scale from zero to 2500 (in intervals, say, of 500).

Label the horizontal axis: 'Atomic number' and extend the scale from zero to 20.

Obtain the necessary ionisation energies from your data book. Label each point with the symbol for the element and join each point to the next by a straight line.

Your graph should clearly show a pattern for the elements of the second period (Li to Ne) which is repeated for those of the third period (Na to Ar).

There is a general increase along a period with discontinuities between Be ($Z = 4$) and B ($Z = 5$) and between N ($Z = 7$) and O ($Z = 8$) in period 2. There are also discontinuities for the corresponding elements in period 3.

 Use your textbook to read about the changes in first ionisation energy across a period. Look for an explanation in terms of:

1. the extent to which inner-shell electrons 'shield' the outer-shell electrons from attraction by the nucleus;
2. the difference in energy between s- and p-orbitals;
3. the difference between removing a paired electron and an unpaired electron.

Note that the so-called stability of half-filled orbitals is not, in itself, an explanation – it is part of the pattern which needs explaining!

Before you do the next exercise, look at Fig. 32. You will recognise that the first part of this graph corresponds to the one that you have drawn in Exercise 84. You will also see that the repeating pattern appears at higher atomic numbers: first ionisation energy is a periodic property of the elements.

Now use Fig. 32 in order to do the next exercise.

Figure 32

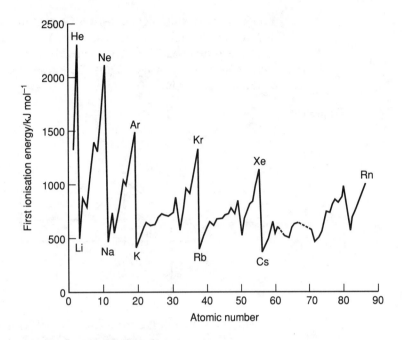

EXERCISE 85

Answers on page 134

Explain the changes in first ionisation energy
a between hydrogen and helium,
b between helium and lithium,
c between beryllium and boron,
d between nitrogen and oxygen,
e along the peaks, Fig. 32 (for the noble gases),
f along the lowest points (for the alkali metals).

At the beginning of Part B, we mentioned two ways of disturbing an atom in order to find out about its electronic structure. We now examine in some detail method **b** – atomic emission spectroscopy.

17 ATOMIC EMISSION SPECTROSCOPY

You know that white light consists of a continuous range of wavelengths which we distinguish by colour. Figure 33 shows a typical arrangement for producing a spectrum. Each line is an image of the slit caused by a particular wavelength of light. If there is a continuous range of wavelengths, the lines merge together into bands of colour in a continuous spectrum.

Figure 33

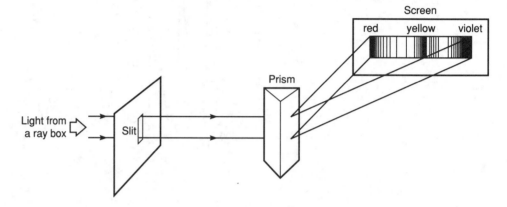

Coloured light emitted from sources such as sodium street lamps, neon lights and coloured flames generally consists of a mixture of a limited number of wavelengths. Emission spectroscopy is concerned with the examination of this sort of emitted radiation.

OBJECTIVE When you have finished this chapter you should be able to:
■ describe the difference between a continuous spectrum and a **line emission spectrum**.

We start this section with an experiment in which you see some common emission spectra for yourself.

EXPERIMENT 6 **Using a hand spectroscope to observe the emission spectra of some s-block elements**

Aim This experiment is designed to give you a qualitative introduction to the spectra emitted by some s-block elements when their atoms are excited by heating samples in a Bunsen flame.

Introduction You use a hand spectroscope to observe the continuous spectrum emitted by the tungsten filament of a light bulb. Using a flame test wire, you then obtain coloured emissions from some s-block elements, view these in turn through the spectroscope and compare them with the continuous spectrum from the tungsten filament.

We recommend that you work in pairs in this experiment. All three operations – preparing the flame test wire, obtaining a brightly coloured flame and having the spectroscope ready to look at the flame for the few moments that it lasts – are fairly tricky and require practice and concentration. We suggest that one person prepares the flame while the other stands ready with the spectroscope. You can then change roles so that you both have a chance to observe each spectrum.

Requirements
- safety spectacles
- fume cupboard with gentle fan
- electric lamp with tungsten filament pearl light bulb
- hand spectroscope
- colour plate of spectra
- Bunsen burner and bench protection sheet
- flame test wire (or tongs and supply of filter paper)
- hydrochloric acid, HCl, concentrated
- boiling tube or other glass container for hydrochloric acid
- small pestle and mortar
- spatulas
- watch glasses

at least three of the following:
- barium chloride, $BaCl_2$ (s)
- calcium chloride, $CaCl_2$ (s)
- lithium chloride, LiCl (s)
- potassium chloride, KCl (s)
- sodium chloride, NaCl (s)
- strontium chloride, $SrCl_2$ (s)

HAZARD WARNING

- **Hydrochloric acid** has a corrosive vapour which irritates and can damage your eyes. Wear safety spectacles and work in the fume cupboard for this experiment.
- **Spectroscope. UNDER NO CIRCUMSTANCES** must you look through this at the sun. If you do so, your eyes may be permanently damaged.

Procedure
1. Switch on the lamp and look at the bulb through the spectroscope. Look for a series of colours, one running into the next. This is a continuous spectrum. Compare what you see with the coloured plate showing the emission spectrum from a tungsten filament.
2. Hold the spectroscope up to a window which does not face the sun. You must **never** point the spectroscope directly at the sun. This could result in permanent damage to your eyes.
   You should see the continuous spectrum of visible light.
3. Light the Bunsen burner – adjust it to get a roaring flame.
4. Dip the flame test wire into concentrated hydrochloric acid, then hold it in the hottest part of the flame. Repeat the process until there is little or no colour from the flame test wire in the flame. You may have to repeat this step several times, especially towards the end of the experiment, but certainly no more than 12 times.

5. Crush a little of the salt to be tested finely with a pestle and mortar and mix with a little concentrated hydrochloric acid on a watch glass. Be careful here – use just enough of the acid to give you a semi-solid 'mush' of crystals.
6. Dip the cleaned flame test wire into the mush of the salt to be tested. Adjust the flame until it is pale blue and hold the wire in it. Your partner should be standing by with the spectroscope and should now look through it at the flame. Look for brightly coloured lines. (*Alternatively*, hold with tongs a piece of filter paper soaked in a solution of the chloride in the Bunsen flame.)

   There are several lines for each element and it will probably not be possible to get them all into view at once. The yellow line in the sodium spectrum is easy to see and will probably persist through the spectra of all the elements you try. You can use this line to help you locate lines on the spectra of the other elements, by looking either to the right or to the left of it. Checking with the coloured plate of spectra will give you an idea of where to look for lines from a particular element.
7. Repeat steps 2–5 with the salts of at least two other elements. Also use the spectroscope on any other vapour lamps which may be available, including street lamps, if there is one in view from the laboratory.

Question
Answers on page 134

What is the difference between a continuous spectrum and a line emission spectrum?

Now that you have examined some spectra, we go on to explain why the coloured bands are produced.

■ 17.1 How do atoms emit light?

In this section, we consider what is happening when atoms give out light. This phenomenon is the basis of emission spectroscopy.

OBJECTIVES

When you have finished this section you should be able to:
■ explain the emission of light by atoms in terms of **excited states**;
■ state the relationship between **wavelength and frequency**;
■ state the relationship between energy and frequency of radiation (**Planck's relationship**).

The process that takes place when atoms of an element are given energy – by heating them in a Bunsen flame, for example, or by passing an electric discharge through a gas at low pressure – is summarised in Fig. 34.

Figure 34

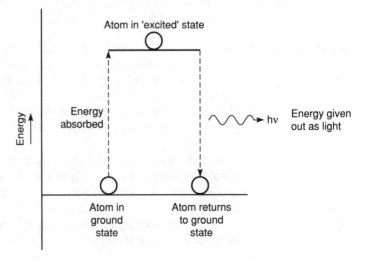

At room temperature, nearly all the atoms in a given sample of substance are in the **ground state**, i.e. the electrons occupy the orbitals of lowest energy.

In a flame, or other energy source, electrons move to orbitals of higher energy. The resulting **excited states** are not stable: each excited electron soon falls to a lower energy state and, in the change, a definite amount of energy, called a quantum, leaves each atom. The energy appears as radiation of a particular wavelength, which may be visible and coloured. The emission spectra you have been looking at consist of a series of coloured lines, each line corresponding to a particular energy drop, from a higher energy level to a lower one. The greater the number of electrons making a particular transition, the more intense the corresponding spectral line.

When you looked at ordinary daylight through a spectroscope, however, you saw a continuous spectrum. In other words, a beam of white light consists of a mixture of coloured beams. The different colours correspond to different values of wavelength, λ (Greek letter *lambda*). Figure 35 indicates the approximate wavelength boundaries and the complete span (400–700 nm) is called the visible range.

Figure 35
Visible spectrum.

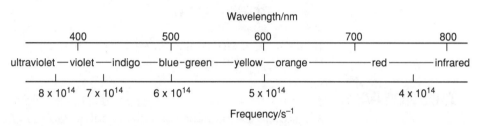

Coloured beams can also be distinguished by their different frequencies. Frequency is represented by the symbol v (Greek letter *nu*, pronounced 'new'). Study the diagram of the spectrum and use it to answer the following exercise.

EXERCISE 86

Answers on page 134

Using the information in Fig. 35, write the relationship between wavelength and frequency
a in words,
b as a mathematical statement.

The proportionality constant is the speed of light, c, so the equation linking wavelength and frequency is:

$$\lambda = \frac{c}{v}, \quad \text{where } c \text{ is the speed of light } (2.998 \times 10^8 \text{ m s}^{-1})$$

All radiation is a form of energy, which can only be transmitted in discrete 'packets' called quanta. The energy of each quantum is proportional to the frequency of the radiation. Figure 36 shows the complete electromagnetic spectrum (of which Fig. 35 represents just the central part). Study it for a few moments and then do the next exercise.

Figure 36
Complete electromagnetic spectrum.

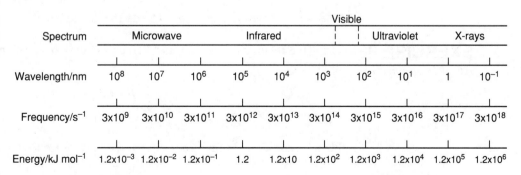

EXERCISE 87
Answers on page 134

Explain why ultraviolet rays are more harmful to our skin than infrared rays.

The relationship between a quantum of energy and the frequency is:

$$E = h\nu$$

where h = Planck's constant and ν = frequency of radiation.
   This important relationship, often called Planck's relationship, has provided the key to finding out the differences between energy levels in atoms, as we shall see in the next section.

■ 17.2 The visible part of the hydrogen emission spectrum

In this section, we examine the visible part of the hydrogen spectrum in detail and relate the energy of light emitted to the electron transitions taking place in the atom.

OBJECTIVES

When you have finished this section you should be able to:
■ calculate the frequency of a given form of radiation using the relationship $\lambda = c/\nu$;
■ calculate the energy associated with a given form of radiation using **Planck's relationship**;
■ explain how the energy of a line in the spectrum relates to the **electron transition** taking place in the atom.

The visible part of the hydrogen spectrum consists of a series of lines which get closer together at shorter wavelengths (higher frequencies). It is known as the Balmer series, after its discoverer. Figure 37 is a diagram of the main lines in this series.

Figure 37
The Balmer series.

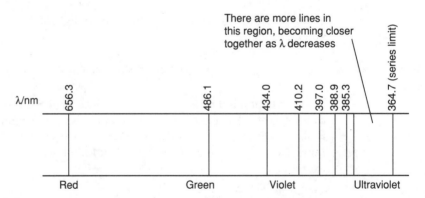

Use the information from Fig. 37 to do the next exercise.

EXERCISE 88
Answers on page 134

Using the relationship $\lambda = c/\nu$ and Planck's equation, calculate the energy of the red line in Fig. 37.

$$h = 6.63 \times 10^{-34} \text{ J s}$$

$$c = 3.00 \times 10^{8} \text{ m s}^{-1}$$

Planck's constant is sometimes quoted with reference to one mole of electron transitions, i.e. 3.99×10^{-13} kJ s mol^{-1}.

The energy you have just calculated is the energy needed to boost an electron from the second energy level to the third. It is given out as a quantum of light, called a photon, when the electron drops back to the second level. Figure 38 shows this electron transition ($n = 3$ to $n = 2$) with its corresponding spectral line; in addition, it shows transitions from higher energy levels to the level $n = 2$ and their corresponding spectral lines. At increasing frequencies, the lines get closer and closer until they merge.

Figure 38
Electron transitions and the
Balmer series.

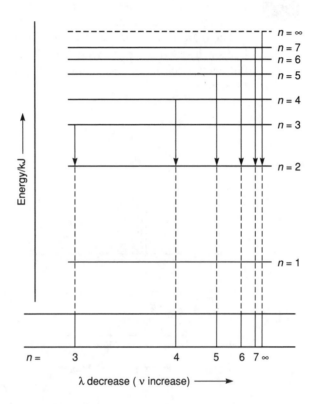

EXERCISE 89
Answers on page 135

a What electron transition corresponds to the point where the spectral lines merge?
b What happens to the electron if $n = \infty$?
c Could you use the energy value at this point to calculate a value for the ionisation energy? Explain.

In the next section, we go on to look at the other series in the hydrogen emission spectrum.

■ 17.3 The complete hydrogen emission spectrum

In this section, we show that each series in the hydrogen spectrum corresponds to a set of electron transitions starting and ending at a different energy level. One of these series can be used to calculate ionisation energy values.

OBJECTIVES

When you have finished this section you should be able to:
■ describe the **emission spectrum** of atomic hydrogen;
■ sketch at least one series of lines from the **hydrogen spectrum**;
■ explain how a hydrogen spectrum is produced.

If it is available, you should now watch the ILPAC video programme 'The Hydrogen Spectrum'.

Read about the emission spectrum of hydrogen in a textbook.

The essential piece of apparatus, **a discharge tube**, contains hydrogen at very low pressure. Look for a description of how a discharge tube is used and the changes that take place inside it.

If the apparatus is available, your teacher may set up a demonstration of the hydrogen emission spectrum for you. If so, you should view it through a hand spectroscope and try and identify some of the lines by comparing them with a photograph or Fig. 37.

The relationship between the various series of lines which go to make up the hydrogen spectrum is shown in Fig. 39. Each series is named after its discoverer. You do not need to learn all these names, but you will find it useful to remember Balmer and Lyman.

Figure 39
The hydrogen spectrum.

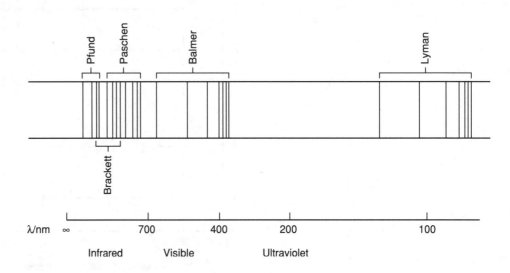

Study the diagram for a few moments and then use it to do the exercise which follows.

EXERCISE 90

Answers on page 135

a In what way are the other series in the hydrogen spectrum similar to the Balmer series?

b Give a simple explanation for this similarity, in terms of energy levels.

The pattern in the spectral lines has been described mathematically by the Rydberg equation:

$$\frac{1}{\lambda} = R_H\left(\frac{1}{n_2^2} - \frac{1}{n_1^2}\right)$$

where λ is the wavelength of the radiation in nm; R_H is a constant, the Rydberg constant. Its value for the hydrogen spectrum is 1.0967758×10^7 m^{-1}. n_1 and n_2 are integers, with the value of n_1 always being greater than n_2.

n_2 represents the electron shell to which the electron is dropping back and n_1 represents the electron shell to which the electron has been promoted. For a given series then, n_2 has a fixed value (in the Balmer series, $n_2 = 2$) and n_1 has a range of values, from $(n_2 + 1)$ to infinity.

Figure 40 shows the relationship between the main series in the hydrogen spectrum and the energy levels with which they are associated.

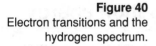

Figure 40
Electron transitions and the
hydrogen spectrum.

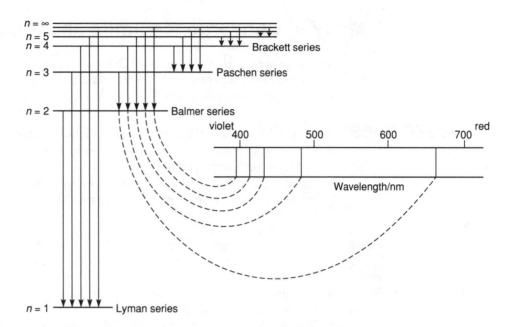

Use the diagram to help you answer the next exercise.

EXERCISE 91

Answers on page 135

Which series of lines in the hydrogen emission spectrum would be suitable for determining its ionisation energy? Give a reason for your answer.

In our study of the hydrogen emission spectrum, you may have been surprised that, so far, we have related the spectral lines to electron transitions between major energy shells in the atom, without mentioning sub-shells. There is a good reason for this. In the hydrogen atom, there is no difference in energy between the sub-levels within a shell. However, in atoms other than hydrogen, the sub-shells are at different energy levels and we can easily demonstrate their existence by emission spectra.

In such multi-electron atoms, many electron transitions, from one orbital to another in different shells, or even within the same shell, are possible. These result in more complex emission spectra consisting of a great many lines.

It is possible to analyse a complex emission spectrum into a large number of converging series like those you have seen for hydrogen, but they are not so obvious because they overlap. At A-level, you will not be asked to interpret in detail anything more complex than the hydrogen spectrum.

In the next section we go on to see how the ionisation energy of hydrogen can be calculated from frequency measurements of the appropriate series of lines in its emission spectrum. The ionisation energy of any element can be calculated using a similar method, but since the details are more complicated, you need only know that it can be done in principle.

■ 17.4 Convergence limits and ionisation energy

You have noticed that the lines in each series in the hydrogen emission spectrum get closer and closer together at higher frequencies. We now make use of this fact to calculate the ionisation energy for hydrogen.

OBJECTIVES

When you have finished this section you should be able to:
■ explain what is meant by the **convergence limit** of a series of lines in the hydrogen emission spectrum;
■ explain how a value for the ionisation energy of hydrogen can be obtained from the convergence limit of the Lyman series.

Read about convergence limits in the hydrogen spectrum and then do the following exercise.

EXERCISE 92
Answers on page 135

a Explain how the convergence limit of the Lyman series can be used to provide a value for the ionisation energy of hydrogen.
b Why would the convergence limit of the Balmer or the Brackett series not be suitable for determining the ionisation energy?

From the convergence limit of the Lyman series the ionisation energy of hydrogen is calculated to be 1314 kJ mol^{-1}.

To help you draw together your ideas about the hydrogen spectrum and its use in determining the structure of the atom, do the Teacher-marked Exercise which follows. After you have looked through your notes, we suggest that you put them away and write your answer in examination conditions, allowing about 30 minutes.

EXERCISE
Teacher-marked

The atomic spectrum of hydrogen is given by the following relationship:

$$\frac{1}{\lambda} = R_H \left(\frac{1}{n_2^2} - \frac{1}{n_1^2} \right)$$

a i) What does λ represent?
ii) What do the terms n_1 and n_2 represent?
iii) What are the units of the constant R_H?
b The spectrum comprises a number of lines which may be divided into a number of series.
i) Why does the spectrum consist of lines?
ii) Why is there a small number of series in the spectrum?
iii) Explain why each series converges and in what direction it converges.
c What method is used to generate the light source for observing the atomic spectrum of hydrogen?
d Name the instrument used to resolve the hydrogen spectrum.

You have now studied some of the theoretical aspects of atomic spectra. In the final chapter you learn how atomic spectroscopy is used for the elemental analysis of materials.

18 APPLICATIONS OF ATOMIC SPECTROSCOPY

In this chapter we describe briefly some of the techniques used in atomic spectroscopy and some of their applications in the analysis of materials.

OBJECTIVE When you have finished this chapter you should be able to:
■ describe some of the analytical applications of atomic spectroscopy.

In Section 17.1 you will have learned that atomic spectra arise from the transitions of electrons between various energy levels in atoms. Since an atom of any one element has energy levels different from those of any other element, it follows that each element has a characteristic spectrum which can be used to identify it, rather like a 'fingerprint'. For example, helium was discovered on the sun by spectroscopy before it was discovered on earth, hence its name (*Helios* is Greek for 'sun').

You will have seen some atomic spectra in Experiment 6.

Thus atomic spectroscopy, both emission and absorption, provides a most useful and important field of analysis. The positions of the spectral lines serve to identify the elements in a substance and their intensities can be used to measure concentration. The instruments are calibrated by using standard materials or solutions of known composition.

Some of the techniques are described below.

■ 18.1 Flame photometry

This is used to determine elements of groups I and II which give coloured flames (and therefore emit in the visible region) and it is widely used to determine sodium and potassium in biological materials, such as blood plasma.

The sample, in the form of a very dilute solution, is sprayed into a Bunsen flame and the light is passed through an optical filter to a photoelectric device which produces an electrical output signal. This is a very simple and cheap arrangement.

■ 18.2 Atomic emission spectrometry (AES)

A modern atomic emission spectrometer operates on the same principles and has basically the same layout as that shown in Fig. 33 but with some important (and expensive!) additions and modifications. For example, many of the most useful lines for identification lie in the ultraviolet region so quartz optics are used instead of glass. Excitation of the sample is done with a DC arc, a high voltage AC spark or, more recently, an inductively coupled plasma torch (ICP) which provides extremely high excitation energies. A diffraction grating is used instead of a prism. The intensities of selected spectral lines are measured by a series of carefully positioned photomultiplier tubes, whose output signals are processed by a computer.

The whole process is extremely fast and as many as 20 or more elements can be determined simultaneously. It has wide application in many fields such as the steel and the non-ferrous metal industries (e.g. for quality control), the analysis of rocks, minerals and other refractory materials.

Atomic emission
spectrometer.

■ 18.3 Atomic absorption spectrometry (AAS)

Figure 34 illustrates the emission of light by atoms when electrons drop back to lower
energy levels but it also shows that when light is absorbed the electrons move up to
higher levels. In both cases the light energy is said to be 'quantised', i.e. it has discrete
values, and so elements may also be analysed by means of their absorption spectra.

Figure 41 is a flow diagram for an atomic absorption spectrometer.

A 'hollow cathode' lamp provides radiation of characteristic wavelengths. The
'atomiser' produces free atoms from the sample, either by an air–acetylene flame or by
an electrothermal device such as a graphite rod. The monochromator isolates the
desired wavelength, the intensity of which is measured by the detector
(a photomultiplier tube).

This method is routinely used for trace metal analysis and is capable of measurement
down to parts per billion. It finds application in a number of fields such as water analysis
and pollution studies.

Figure 41
Atomic absorption
spectrometer – flow diagram.

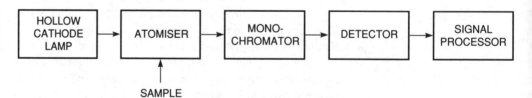

Use the above information to help you answer the following exercise.

EXERCISE 93
Answers on page 135

a Steel samples from a foundry are routinely analysed for minor constituents such as
carbon, phosphorus, manganese, etc. Many years ago this was done by 'wet' chemical
methods which could take one or two days to complete but now of course it is done in
minutes by atomic emission spectrometry.

Suggest two ways in which this change has reduced costs.

b Suggest why a flame photometer would be used instead of an atomic emission
spectrometer in a medical laboratory.

Check that you have adequate notes before going on to the End-of-unit test.

■ End-of-unit test

To find out how well you have learned the material in this unit, try the test which follows. Read the notes below before starting.

■ You should spend about 90 minutes on this test.
■ You will need a sheet of graph paper.
■ Hand your answers to your teacher for marking.

Questions 1–3 concern the first six ionisation energies for the elements A to E below:

	1st	2nd	3rd	4th	5th	6th	ionisation energy (kJ mol^{-1})
A	1090	2350	4610	6220	37800	47000	
B	1400	2860	4590	7480	9400	53200	
C	494	4560	6940	9540	13400	16600	
D	736	1450	7740	10500	13600	18000	
E	1310	3390	5320	7450	11000	13300	

Select from A to E, the element which is most likely to
1. be in group IV of the Periodic Table, (1)
2. form a chloride of the type MCl$_2$, (1)
3. form a compound of the type Na$_2$M. (1)

Directions For questions 4, 5 and 6 **one** or **more** of the responses are correct. Decide which of the responses is (are) correct. Then choose:
A if **1, 2** and **3** are all correct,
B if **1** and **2** only are correct,
C if **2** and **3** only are correct,
D if **1** only is correct,
E if **3** only is correct.

Directions summarised				
A	B	C	D	E
1, 2, 3	**1, 2**	**2, 3**	**1**	**3**
correct	only	only	only	only

4. A mass spectrometer is operated under conditions of high vacuum to
   1 keep the magnetic field constant,
   2 minimise the formation of O$_2^+$ and N$_2^+$ ions,
   3 minimise collisions between ions and molecules. (1)

5. The first ionisation energy of sulphur is **less** than the first ionisation energy of
   1 argon,
   2 neon,
   3 oxygen. (1)

6. The element with atomic number 18 has a relative atomic mass of 40 and electronic structure 1s^{2}2s^{2}2p^{6}3s^{2}3p^6. It follows that the element with atomic number 19
   1 forms ions of electronic structure 1s^{2}2s^{2}2p^{6}3s^{2}3p^6,
   2 has electronic structure 1s^{2}2s^{2}2p^{6}3s^{2}3p^{6}4s^1,
   3 has a relative atomic mass of 41. (1)

Questions 7 and 8 are followed by five suggested answers. Select the best answer in each case.

7. The first ionisation energy for carbon is greater than it is for sodium. One of the factors responsible is that
   A the nuclear charge on carbon is greater,
   B the outer quantum shell is further from the nucleus in carbon atoms than in sodium atoms,
   C the number of electrons in the outer quantum shell of carbon is greater than in sodium,
   D the shielding provided by the inner quantum shells in sodium is greater,
   E the interatomic bonding in graphite and diamond is stronger than in metallic sodium. (1)

8. The ground-state electronic configurations of five elements are shown below. For which element would you expect the value of the first ionisation energy to be the greatest?

   1s   2s   2p
A [↑] [ ] [| |]

   1s   2s   2p
D [↑↓] [↑↓] [| |]

B [↑↓] [ ] [| |]

E [↑↓] [↑↓] [↑ | |]

C [↑↓] [↑] [| |]   (1)

9. The first seven types of orbital permitted for any atom are, in random order, 2s, 3p, 4s, 3d, 1s, 2p, 3s.
   If the atom is Ca, write down the orbitals in order of increasing energy (from left to right) and give the number of electrons in each orbital. (2)

10. a Sketch a line spectrum of hydrogen (Lyman series only, wavelength increasing from left to right). (2)
    b The charge on the oxygen nucleus is eight times that on the hydrogen nucleus and yet the first ionisation energies of hydrogen and oxygen are almost identical (1300 kJ mol^{-1}). Suggest reasons for this. (2)

11. In Table 12 below, the first, second and third ionisation energies of six successive elements in the Periodic Table are listed. The elements have been arbitrarily denoted by the letters A to F. All energy values are given in kJ mol^{-1}.

Table 12	A	B	C	D	E	F
First ionisation energy	1013	1000	1255	1519	418	590
Second ionisation energy	1904	2255	2297	2665	3067	1146
Third ionisation energy	2916	3389	3853	3933	4393	4916

a i) Which one of the elements A to F is likely to be a noble gas?
   ii) Give reason(s) for your answer. (2)
b In the light of your answer to **a**, suggest the names of a set of chemical elements that could be represented by A to F. (2)
c State the equation representing the processes to which the ionisation energies refer. Use the symbol Z to denote the element. (3)

12. The first ionisation energies of the elements lithium to neon, in kJ mol^{-1}, are given below.

Li	Be	B	C	N	O	F	Ne
519	900	799	1090	1400	1310	1680	2080

a Write an equation representing the first ionisation energy of oxygen. (1)

b i) Explain why the ionisation energies show an overall tendency to increase across the period.

ii) Explain the irregularities in this trend for boron and for oxygen. (6)

c An element X has successive ionisation energies as follows:

786;   1580;   3230;   4360;   16 000;   20 000;   23 600;   29 100 kJ mol^{-1}

i) To which group in the Periodic Table does X belong? Explain your answer.

ii) Write down the outer electronic configuration of an atom of X.

iii) Suggest formulae for **two** chlorides of X. (5)

d Chlorine consists of two isotopes having mass numbers 35 and 37 of relative abundance 75% and 25%, respectively. The questions below relate to the mass spectrum of a sample of gaseous chlorine.

i) How many peaks would you expect in the m/e range 34–38? What would be the m/e value of the most intense peak in this range? (Consider singly charged ions only.)

ii) How many peaks corresponding to ions of type Cl_2^+ would you expect to observe? (Consider singly charged ions only.) Give the m/e value of each and identify the most intense peak. (5)

13.

Figure 42

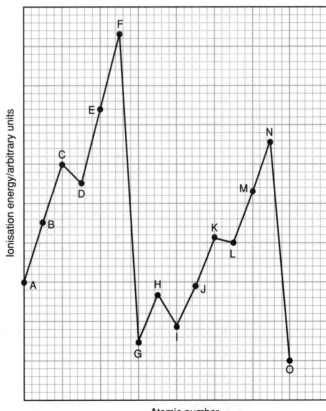

The graph in Fig. 42 shows the first ionisation energies of 15 successive elements in the Periodic Table, lettered A to O, all with atomic numbers less than 25.

a Using the letters A to O as appropriate (and not the chemical symbols which you know or think these letters represent) select:
   i) two alkali metals (group 1 metals);
   ii) an element which forms no true chemical compounds. (2)

b Although the graph shows an overall rise in first ionisation energy from element G to element N, the value for element I is lower than for element H. How may this be explained? (2)

c On graph paper (see Fig. 43), sketch the graph showing the first six successive ionisation energies of the element G. (2)

d All the elements A to O have some electrons in s-orbitals. Describe, by a diagram or otherwise, the distribution of electron density round the nucleus for an s-orbital. (2)

e Which of the elements A to O are in the s-block and which in the p-block? (2)

Figure 43

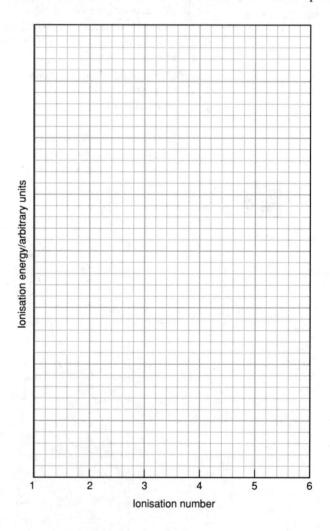

Ionisation energy/arbitrary units

Ionisation number

14. Identify A, B, and C in the following equations:

a $^{234}_{92}U \rightarrow \alpha + A$

b $^{239}_{92}U \rightarrow \beta + B$

c $^{235}_{92}U \rightarrow \gamma + C$ (3)

15. Table 13 contains some information concerning element X, of atomic number 31. In its natural state, it consists of a mixture of two isotopes, X_A and X_B. Its first four ionisation energies are 580, 2000, 3000 and 6200 kJ mol^{-1}.

Table 13

Isotope	Isotopic mass	Percentage abundance
X_A	69.0	60.2
X_B	71.0	39.8

a Calculate a value for the relative atomic mass of X correct to three significant figures. (3)

b i) Write down the electronic configuration (in terms of s, p and d levels) of element X in its ground state.

ii) In which group of the Periodic Table is X placed? (2)

c Explain why:

i) the difference between the first and second ionisation energies is greater than that between the second and third ionisation energies; (2)

ii) the difference between the third and fourth ionisation energies is much larger than that between the other successive energies. (2)

(Total: 60 marks)

APPENDIX: A historical perspective

So far in this unit we have not included a historical account of the work which led to the models of atomic structure we have outlined. This is partly because you can understand something without knowing the details of its historical development and partly because few examination boards require such knowledge.

However, we hope you will be interested to read about some of the work that was done – particularly since the turn of the century – and consider its implications for society today. This appendix provides a brief account.

Check with your teacher whether your examination board does require any historical knowledge. As a guide, we include some typical examination questions in this subject area which you should try, if appropriate.

■ Chronological table of some important developments in atomic theory

1803 – Dalton's theory of identical atoms
1884 – Balmer observed the visible spectrum of hydrogen
1896 – Becquerel discovered radioactivity
1897 – Thomson discovered the electron
1911 – Rutherford proposed the nuclear atom
1913 – Moseley defined atomic number; Rutherford and Soddy discovered isotopes; Bohr's theory of planetary electrons in atoms
1919 – Rutherford transmuted ^{14}N to ^{17}O by α bombardment
1932 – Chadwick characterised neutrons in beam from Be by α bombardment
1939 – Hahn and Strassmann discovered atomic fission
1945 – Hiroshima and Nagasaki destroyed by fission bombs
1952 – Nuclear fusion bomb (hydrogen bomb) at Bikini Atoll
1956 – First nuclear fission power-station, Calder Hall, Cumbria
1960s – Attempts to harness nuclear fusion; the hunting of the quark
1970s – Development of theories of matter particles based on quarks and leptons
1980s – Discovery of bosons; search for 'grand universal theory'.

■ Dalton's atomic theory

Dalton was not the first to propose that matter was particulate rather than continuous. The Greek philosopher, Democritus, in 400 BC, suggested that there were unsplittable particles which we now call atoms (from the Greek a = not, *tomos* = I cut) and in the seventeenth century Isaac Newton said 'It seems probable to me that God in the beginning formed matter in solid, massy, hard, impenetrable, moveable particles, of such sizes, and figures, and with such other properties, and in such proportion, as most conduced to the end for which He formed them.'

However, Dalton was the first to base an atomic theory on experiment. At the birth of modern chemistry in the late eighteenth century, when many new elements were being discovered by Priestley, Scheele, Davy and others, John Dalton (working in Manchester) identified the 'laws of chemical combination by weight'. These included the law of conservation of matter, the law of constant composition and the law of multiple proportions; and they could be explained by his atomic theory.

For further information on these laws, you should consult older textbooks. You may also be interested in trying experiments to illustrate the laws, in which case you should consult your teacher.

Dalton's theory had its weaknesses. He thought water was HO, he did not know about isotopes and he did not foresee the 'splitting of the atom' by twentieth century nuclear physicists.

Look at the propositions of Dalton's atomic theory and suggest how each one might be modified in the light of modern knowledge. Bear in mind, however, that his simple 'model' of matter is still quite useful both as a first introduction to the subject and also in topics where a more sophisticated model is not necessary. An example of the latter is the kinetic theory of gases which you will study in a later unit.

■ The discovery of the electron

 Read about the work of Crookes and J. J. Thomson on 'cathode rays' which they observed when an electrical discharge was passed through a gas at low pressure. The properties of these rays showed them to consist of particles, each very much smaller than an atom and with a negative charge.

■ The Geiger–Marsden experiment

Geiger and Marsden, working under the direction of Lord Rutherford, employed a stream of α particles from a radioactive source for bombarding a thin sheet of gold or other metal. They found that most of the particles went straight through, but that a small fraction rebounded, as shown in Fig. 44.

Figure 44
The Geiger–Marsden
experiment.

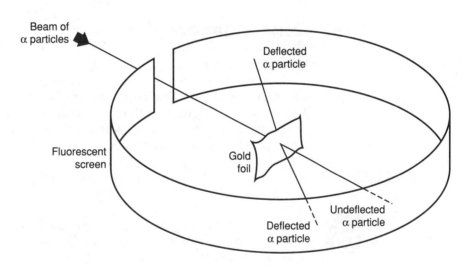

 Read about this experiment to understand how it showed that the material in gold atoms is concentrated in compact nuclei, like stones in plums. Rutherford suggested the nuclei were positively charged and the outer regions contained electrons of compensating negative charge and, as you have already learned, this model was further elaborated by Bohr and others.

■ Moseley's experiment

In 1913, Moseley showed that there were no gaps in the first 40 or so elements in the Periodic Table. He obtained X-rays from each element in turn and found their frequencies by diffracting them, using a crystal of potassium hexacyanoferrate(III) (also known as potassium ferricyanide), as shown in Fig. 45.

Figure 45
Moseley's experiment.

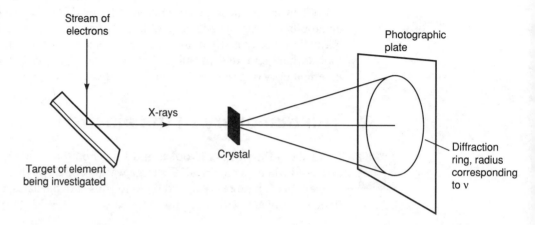

Find out how the variation of the frequency of the X-rays with the identity of the element showed that atomic number Z is a fundamental characteristic of an element and not just the position of that element in a list. Also, look for the reasoning which showed that there were no gaps in the first 40 or so elements in the Periodic Table.

Together with the discovery of isotopes at about the same time, Moseley's work led to the search for the neutron which, however, was not finally identified for nearly 20 years.

■ Consolidation

To consolidate your reading, you should now attempt the following Teacher-marked Exercise, which consists of parts of three A-level questions. This exercise is designed to help you organise your ideas about certain aspects of the history of atomic structure. Before you start writing, read through any notes you have made and check over any points you are not sure about in a suitable book. Then put away your notes and allow about 45 minutes to write an answer.

EXERCISE
Teacher-marked

a Summarise the observations which led to the discovery of the electron. On what experimental evidence is the electron regarded as being both particle-like and wave-like in nature?

b For each of the following classical experiments, describe briefly what was done, what was observed, and what was deduced:
   i) Geiger and Marsden's experiment;
   ii) Moseley's experiment.

c Describe in outline how a beam of neutrons can be produced. State briefly what experimental evidence led to the conclusion that a neutron has
   i) no electric charge;
   ii) a mass approximately equal to that of the proton.

ANSWERS

■ Answers for unit – The Mole

(Answers to questions from examination papers are provided by ILPAC and not by the examination boards.)

EXERCISE 1

Results Table 1

Element	Relative atomic mass (RAM)		
	H scale	O scale	^{12}C scale
H	1.00000	1.00794	1.00790
He	3.97123	4.00276	4.00260
Li	6.88459	6.93924	6.93897
C	11.9169	12.0115	12.0111
O	15.8740	16.0000	15.9994
Na	22.8096	22.9907	22.9898
Ar	39.6349	39.9496	39.9480
U	236.164	238.039	238.030

EXERCISE 2

$$\text{amount} = \frac{\text{mass}}{\text{mass per dozen}} = \frac{5265 \text{ g}}{45.0 \text{ g doz}^{-1}} = 125 \text{ doz}$$

EXERCISE 3

a

$$\text{amount} = \frac{\text{mass}}{\text{mass per gross}} = \frac{5.13 \times 10^6 \text{ g}}{82.08 \text{ g gross}^{-1}}$$

$$= 6.25 \times 10^4 \text{ gross}$$

b

$$\text{number} = \text{amount} \times \text{number per amount} = 6.25 \times 10^4 \text{ gross} \times 144 \text{ gross}^{-1}$$
$$= 9.00 \times 10^6$$

EXERCISE 4

a

$$\text{time} = \frac{\text{number of molecules}}{\text{rate of removal}} = \frac{1.67 \times 10^{23}}{1 \text{ s}^{-1}}$$

$$= 1.67 \times 10^{23} \text{ s}$$

b

$$1 \text{ y} = 365 \text{ dy} \times \frac{24 \text{ h}}{\text{dy}} \times \frac{60 \text{ min}}{\text{h}} \times \frac{60 \text{ s}}{\text{min}} = 3.15 \times 10^7 \text{ s}$$

$$\therefore 1 \text{ s} = \frac{1 \text{ y}}{3.15 \times 10^7}$$

$$\therefore \text{ time taken} = 1.67 \times 10^{23} \text{ s}$$

$$= 1.67 \times 10^{23} \times \frac{1 \text{ y}}{3.15 \times 10^7} = 5.30 \times 10^{15} \text{ y}$$

EXERCISE 5

a 17.0 g mol^{-1} $14.0 + 3(1.0) = 17.0$
b 199.9 g mol^{-1} $40.1 + 2(79.9) = 199.9$
c 98.0 g mol^{-1} $3(1.0) + 31.0 + 4(16.0) = 98.0$
d 322.1 g mol^{-1} $2(23.0) + 32.1 + 4(16.0) + 20(1.0) + 10(16.0) = 322.1$

EXERCISE 6 **a** 35.5 g
b 71.0 g
c 31.0 g
d 124.0 g
e 126.9 g (ignore the mass of the extra electrons)

EXERCISE 7 **a** Substituting into the expression

$$n = \frac{m}{M}$$

where $m = 30.0$ g and $M = 32.0$ g mol^{-1}

gives
$$n = \frac{m}{M} = \frac{30.0 \text{ g}}{32.0 \text{ g mol}^{-1}} = 0.938 \text{ mol}$$

b
$$n = \frac{m}{M} = \frac{31.0 \text{ g}}{124.0 \text{ g mol}^{-1}} = 0.250 \text{ mol}$$

c
$$n = \frac{m}{M} = \frac{50.0 \text{ g}}{100.0 \text{ g mol}^{-1}} = 0.500 \text{ mol}$$

EXERCISE 8 **a** Substituting into the expression

$$n = \frac{m}{M} \text{ in the form } m = nM$$

where $n = 1.00$ mol and $M = 2.00$ g mol^{-1}
gives $m = nM = 1.00$ mol $\times$ 2.00 g mol^{-1} = 2.00 g
b $m = nM = 0.500$ mol $\times$ 58.5 g mol^{-1} = 29.3 g
c $m = nM = 0.250$ mol $\times$ 44.0 g mol^{-1} = 11.0 g

EXERCISE 9 **a** Substituting into the expression

$$n = \frac{m}{M}$$

where $m = 1.00$ g, $M = 17.0$ g mol^{-1}

gives
$$n = \frac{m}{M} = \frac{1.00 \text{ g}}{17.0 \text{ g mol}^{-1}} = 0.0588 \text{ mol}$$

b If the number of molecules is to be the same, then the amount must be the same. For SO_2, $M = 64.1$ g mol^{-1} and from **a**, $n = 0.0588$ mol.
∴ substituting these values in the expression

$$n = \frac{m}{M} = \text{ in the form } m = nM$$

gives $m = nM = 0.0588$ mol $\times$ 64.1 g mol^{-1} = 3.77 g

EXERCISE 10 **a** Substituting into the expression

$$n = \frac{m}{M}$$

where $m = 18.0$ g, $M = 12.0$ g mol^{-1}

gives

$$n = \frac{m}{M} = \frac{18.0 \text{ g}}{12.0 \text{ g mol}^{-1}} = 1.50 \text{ mol}$$

Substituting into the expression

$$N = nL$$

where $n = 1.50$ mol, $L = 6.02 \times 10^{23}$ mol^{-1}
gives $N = nL = 1.50$ mol $\times 6.02 \times 10^{23}$ mol^{-1} $= 9.03 \times 10^{23}$

Or, substituting $n = \dfrac{m}{M}$ into the expression $N = nL$

gives

$$N = \frac{mL}{M} = \frac{18.0 \text{ g} \times 6.02 \times 10^{23} \text{ mol}^{-1}}{12.0 \text{ g mol}^{-1}} = 9.03 \times 10^{23}$$

b

$$N = \frac{mL}{M} = \frac{18.0 \text{ g} \times 6.02 \times 10^{23} \text{ mol}^{-1}}{63.5 \text{ g mol}^{-1}} = 1.71 \times 10^{23}$$

c

$$N = \frac{mL}{M} = \frac{7.20 \text{ g} \times 6.02 \times 10^{23} \text{ mol}^{-1}}{32.1 \text{ g mol}^{-1}} = 1.35 \times 10^{23}$$

Note that in **c** the number of **atoms** is the same whatever the molecular formula.

EXERCISE 11 **a** Substituting into the expression

$$n = \frac{m}{M}$$

where $m = 1.00$ g, $M = 17.0$ g mol^{-1}

gives

$$n = \frac{1.00 \text{ g}}{17.0 \text{ g mol}^{-1}} = 0.0588 \text{ mol}$$

Substituting into the expression

$$N = nL$$

gives $N = 0.0588$ mol $\times 6.02 \times 10^{23}$ mol^{-1} $= 3.54 \times 10^{22}$

Or, combining $n = \dfrac{m}{M}$ with $N = nL$ and substituting gives

$$N = \frac{mL}{M} = \frac{1.00 \text{ g} \times 6.02 \times 10^{23} \text{ mol}^{-1}}{17.0 \text{ g mol}^{-1}} = 3.54 \times 10^{22}$$

b
$$N = \frac{mL}{M} = \frac{3.28 \text{ g} \times 6.02 \times 10^{23} \text{ mol}^{-1}}{64.1 \text{ g mol}^{-1}} = 3.08 \times 10^{22}$$

c
$$N = \frac{mL}{M} = \frac{7.20 \text{ g} \times 6.02 \times 10^{23} \text{ mol}^{-1}}{8 \times 32.1 \text{ g mol}^{-1}} = 1.69 \times 10^{22}$$

EXERCISE 12 **a** 0.500 mol of NaCl contains 0.500 mol of Na^+ and 0.500 mol of Cl^-
∴ Total amount of ions, $n = 1.00$ mol
Substituting into the expression

$$N = nL$$

gives $N = 1.00 \text{ mol} \times 6.02 \times 10^{23} \text{ mol}^{-1} = 6.02 \times 10^{23}$
b The amount of NaCl is calculated by substituting into the expression

$$n = \frac{m}{M}$$

where $m = 14.6$ g and $M = 58.5$ g mol^{-1}

$$\therefore n = \frac{14.6 \text{ g}}{58.5 \text{ g mol}^{-1}} = 0.250 \text{ mol}$$

0.250 mol of NaCl contains 0.250 mol of Na^+ and 0.250 mol of Cl^-
∴ total amount of ions, $n = 0.500$ mol
Substituting into the expression

$$N = nL$$

gives $N = 0.500 \text{ mol} \times 6.02 \times 10^{23} \text{ mol}^{-1} = 3.01 \times 10^{23}$
c The amount of $CaCl_2$ is given by substituting in the expression

$$n = \frac{m}{M}$$

where $m = 18.5$ g and $M = 111.0$ g mol^{-1}

$$\therefore n = \frac{18.5 \text{ g}}{111.0 \text{ g mol}^{-1}} = 0.167 \text{ mol}$$

Since each mole of $CaCl_2$ contains 3 mol of ions (Ca^{2+}, Cl^-, Cl^-), the amount of ions, $n = 3 \times 0.167 \text{ mol} = 0.501 \text{ mol}$
Substituting into the expression

$$N = nL$$

gives $N = 0.501 \text{ mol} \times 6.02 \times 10^{23} \text{ mol}^{-1} = 3.02 \times 10^{23}$

EXPERIMENT 1

Specimen results and calculations

Results Table 2

Number of drops to deliver 1 cm³ of solution	Number of drops delivered to make monomolecular layer	Diameter of monomolecular layer/cm
100	12	11.2

1.
$$\text{Volume of 1 drop} = \frac{1.0 \text{ cm}^3}{100} = 0.010 \text{ cm}^3$$

2. Since 1000 cm³ of solution contains 0.050 cm³ of oleic acid

$$1.00 \text{ cm}^3 \text{ of solution contains } \frac{0.050 \text{ cm}^3}{1000} \text{ of oleic acid}$$

$$\therefore 0.010 \text{ cm}^3 \text{ of solution contains } \frac{0.050 \text{ cm}^3 \times 0.010}{1000} \text{ of oleic acid} = 5.0 \times 10^{-7} \text{ cm}^3$$

3. Volume of oleic acid in monomolecular layer = 5.0×10^{-7} cm³ × 12 = 6.0×10^{-6} cm³

4.
$$A = \frac{3.142 \times (11.2 \text{ cm})^2}{4} = 98.5 \text{ cm}^2$$

5.
$$\text{Thickness } = \frac{\text{volume}}{\text{area}} = \frac{6.0 \times 10^{-6} \text{cm}^3}{98.5 \text{ cm}^2} = 6.1 \times 10^{-8} \text{ cm}$$

6. Volume of one molecule = $(6.1 \times 10^{-8} \text{ cm})^3 = 2.3 \times 10^{-22} \text{ cm}^3$

7.
$$\text{Density } = \frac{\text{molar mass}}{\text{molar volume}}$$

$$\therefore \text{molar volume} = \frac{\text{molar mass}}{\text{density}} = \frac{282 \text{ g mol}^{-1}}{0.890 \text{ g cm}^{-3}} = 317 \text{ cm}^3 \text{ mol}^{-1}$$

8.
$$L = \frac{\text{molar volume}}{\text{volume of molecule}} = \frac{317 \text{ cm}^3 \text{ mol}^{-1}}{2.3 \times 10^{-22} \text{ cm}^3} = 1.4 \times 10^{24} \text{ mol}^{-1}$$

(The accepted value of $L = 6.02 \times 10^{23}$ mol⁻¹. You should expect to obtain a value of L to within one power of 10, i.e. between 6.0×10^{22} mol⁻¹ and 6.0×10^{24} mol⁻¹.)

EXPERIMENT 1

Questions

1. The various sources of error which may account for the difference between the experimental and actual value for L are as follows:
    a the number of drops required to make a monomolecular layer was inaccurately measured;
    b not all the pentane had evaporated from the surface;
    c the volume of the drop was inaccurately determined;
    d the molecules were unevenly dispersed on the surface of the film, i.e. there was more than one layer of molecules on parts of the film;
    e the assumption about the shape of the molecule was incorrect. In fact, the molecule is rather more the shape of a cylinder than a cube.

2. The number of drops required to fill the loop is subject to the greatest error. Even if you are sure to the nearest drop, this gives only two significant figures (or only one for a small loop!) whereas all the other values are obtained to three significant figures.
3. A substitute for pentane must:
    a dissolve oleic acid readily;
    b evaporate readily;
    c not react with oleic acid;
    d not react with water;
    e not dissolve in water.

EXERCISE 13   a From the equation for the reaction we know that

$$\text{amount of Mg} = \text{amount of S}$$

The amount of S is found by using the expression

$$n = \frac{m}{M}$$

where $m = 16.0$ g and $M = 32.1$ g mol^{-1}

$$\therefore n = \frac{m}{M} = \frac{16.0 \text{ g}}{32.1 \text{ g mol}^{-1}} = 0.498 \text{ mol}$$

$\therefore$ the amount of Mg also $= 0.498$ mol.
The mass of Mg is found by using the expression

$$n = \frac{m}{M} \text{ in the form } m = nM$$

where $n = 0.498$ mol and $M = 24.3$ g mol^{-1},
$\therefore m = nM = 0.498$ mol $\times 24.3$ g mol$^{-1} = 12.1$ g

b For NaNO$_3$, $n = \dfrac{m}{M} = \dfrac{4.25 \text{ g}}{85.0 \text{ g mol}^{-1}} = 0.0500$ mol

But amount of O$_2$ = ½ × amount of NaNO$_3$
                    = ½ × 0.0500 mol = 0.0250 mol
For O$_2$, $m = nM$ = 0.0250 mol × 32.0 g mol^{-1} = 0.800 g

EXERCISE 14   For P, substituting into the expression

$$n = \frac{m}{M}$$

where $m = 4.00$ g and $M = 31.0$ g mol^{-1}

gives $n = \dfrac{m}{M} = \dfrac{4.00 \text{ g}}{31.0 \text{ g mol}^{-1}} = 0.129$ mol

From the equation

$$\frac{\text{amount of } P_2O_5}{\text{amount of } P} = \frac{2}{4} = \frac{1}{2}$$

$$\therefore \text{amount of } P_2O_5 = \frac{1}{2} \times \text{amount of } P$$

$$= \frac{1}{2} \times 0.129 \text{ mol} = 0.0645 \text{ mol}$$

For P_2O_5, substituting into the expression

$$n = \frac{m}{M} \text{ in the form } m = nM$$

where $n = 0.0645$ mol and $M = 142$ g mol^{-1}
gives $m = 0.0645 \text{ mol} \times 142 \text{ g mol}^{-1} = 9.16$ g.

EXERCISE 15 The reacting amount of Al is given by substituting into the expression

$$n = \frac{m}{M}$$

where $m = 0.27$ g and $M = 27.0$ g mol^{-1}

$$\therefore \ n = \frac{0.27 \text{ g}}{27.0 \text{ g mol}^{-1}} = 0.010 \text{ mol}$$

The amount of Cu formed is given by substituting into the expression

$$n = \frac{m}{M}$$

where $m = 0.96$ g and $M = 63.8$ g mol^{-1}

$$\therefore \ n = \frac{0.96 \text{ g}}{63.5 \text{ g mol}^{-1}} = 0.015 \text{ mol}$$

$$\therefore \ \frac{\text{amount of Al}}{\text{amount of Cu}} = \frac{0.010 \text{ mol}}{0.015 \text{ mol}} = \frac{2}{3}$$

We can build up the equation from this ratio

$$2Al \text{ (s)} + ? \ CuSO_4 \text{ (aq)} \rightarrow 3Cu \text{ (s)} + ? \ Al_2(SO_4)_3 \text{ (aq)}$$

To equalise Cu atoms, the stoichiometric coefficient for $CuSO_4$ must be 3.
To equalise Al atoms, the stoichiometric coefficient for $Al_2(SO_4)_3$ must be 1.

$$\therefore \ 2Al \text{ (s)} + 3CuSO_4 \text{ (aq)} \rightarrow 3Cu \text{ (s)} + Al_2(SO_4)_3 \text{ (aq)}$$

EXERCISE 16 We must calculate the amount of each reagent to determine which limits the reaction. For Fe, substituting into the expression

$$n = \frac{m}{M}$$

where $m = 2.8$ g and $M = 55.8$ g mol^{-1}

gives

$$n = \frac{2.8 \text{ g}}{55.8 \text{ g mol}^{-1}} = 0.050 \text{ mol}$$

For S, substituting into the expression

$$n = \frac{m}{M}$$

where $m = 2.0$ g and $M = 32.1$ g mol^{-1}

gives

$$n = \frac{2.0 \text{ g}}{32.1 \text{ g mol}^{-1}} = 0.062 \text{ mol}$$

From the equation, one mole of iron reacts with one mole of sulphur, so the amount of iron limits the amount of iron(II) sulphide formed

$$\therefore \text{ amount of FeS} = \text{amount of Fe} = 0.050 \text{ mol}$$

Substituting into the expression

$$n = \frac{m}{M} \text{ in the form } m = nM$$

where $n = 0.050$ mol and $M = 87.9$ g mol^{-1}
gives $m = 0.050$ mol $\times$ 87.9 g mol^{-1} = 4.4 g

EXERCISE 17

	Co	S	O	H$_2$O
Mass/g	2.10	1.14	2.28	4.5
Molar mass/g mol^{-1}	58.9	32.1	16.0	18.0
Amount/mol	$\frac{2.10}{58.9} = 0.0357$	$\frac{1.14}{32.1} = 0.0355$	$\frac{2.28}{16.0} = 0.143$	$\frac{4.50}{18.0} = 0.250$
Amount/ smallest amount = relative amount	$\frac{0.0357}{0.0355} = 1.01$	$\frac{0.0355}{0.0355} = 1.00$	$\frac{0.143}{0.0355} = 4.03$	$\frac{0.250}{0.0355} = 7.04$
Simplest ratio	1	1	4	7

The formula is CoSO$_4$·7H$_2$O.

EXERCISE 18

	$BaCl_2$	H_2O
Mass/g	8.53	1.47
Molar mass/g mol^{-1}	208.2	18.0
Amount/mol	$\dfrac{8.53}{208.2} = 0.0410$	$\dfrac{1.47}{18.0} = 0.817$
Amount/ smallest amount = relative amount	$\dfrac{0.0410}{0.0410} = 1.00$	$\dfrac{0.0817}{0.0410} = 1.99$
Simplest ratio	1	2

The formula is $BaCl_2 \cdot 2H_2O$, i.e. $x = 2$.

EXERCISE 19 The mass of water removed = 0.585 g – 0.535 g = 0.050 g

	$UO(C_2O_4) \cdot 6H_2O$	H_2O (removed)
Mass/g	0.585	0.050
Molar mass/g mol^{-1}	450	18.0
Amount/mol	$\dfrac{0.585}{450} = 0.00130$	$\dfrac{0.050}{18.0} = 0.0028$
Amount/ smallest amount = relative amount	$\dfrac{0.00130}{0.00130} = 1.00$	$\dfrac{0.0028}{0.0013} = 2.2$
Simplest ratio	1	2

Thus, the ratio of the amount of original compound to the removed water is 1 : 2. This means that for every 1 mol of compound, 2 mol of water were removed. The resulting substance would therefore have the formula $UO(C_2O_4) \cdot 4H_2O$.

EXERCISE 20

	C	H	O
Mass/g	40.0	6.6	53.4
Molar mass/g mol^{-1}	12.0	1.0	16.0
Amount/mol	$\dfrac{40.0}{12.0} = 33.3$	$\dfrac{6.6}{1.0} = 6.6$	$\dfrac{53.4}{16.0} = 3.34$
Amount/ smallest amount = relative amount	$\dfrac{3.33}{3.33} = 1.00$	$\dfrac{6.6}{3.33} = 2.0$	$\dfrac{3.34}{3.33} = 1.00$
Simplest ratio	1	2	1

The empirical formula is CH_2O.

EXERCISE 21

	Na	Al	Si	O	H_2O
Mass/g	12.1	14.2	22.1	42.1	9.48
Molar mass/ g mol^{-1}	23.0	27.0	28.1	16.0	18.0
Amount/mol	$\frac{12.1}{23.0}=0.526$	$\frac{14.2}{27.0}=0.526$	$\frac{22.1}{28.1}=0.786$	$\frac{42.1}{16.0}=2.63$	$\frac{9.48}{18.0}=0.527$
Amount/ smallest amount = relative amount	$\frac{0.526}{0.526}=1.01$	$\frac{0.526}{0.526}=1.00$	$\frac{0.786}{0.526}=1.49$	$\frac{2.63}{0.526}=5.00$	$\frac{0.527}{0.526}=1.00$
Simplest ratio	2	2	3	10	2

Note: Since 1.49 is very close to 1.5, we are justified in rounding up.
The empirical formula is $Na_2Al_2Si_3O_{10}\cdot 2H_2O$.

EXERCISE 22

	C	H	O
Mass/g	3.91	0.87	5.22
Molar mass/g mol^{-1}	12.0	1.0	16.0
Amount/mol	0.326	0.87	0.326
Amount/ smallest amount = relative amount	$\frac{0.326}{0.326}=1.00$	$\frac{0.87}{0.326}=2.67$	$\frac{0.326}{0.326}=1.00$
Simplest ratio	3	8	3

Note: We are not justified in rounding off 2.67 to 3. The number 2.67 is the decimal equivalent of 8/3, so we treble the relative amounts, thus converting 2.67 to 8. The resulting empirical formula is $C_3H_8O_3$.

EXERCISE 23   a Substituting into the expression

$$c=\frac{n}{V}$$

where n =0.100 mol and V = (2000/1000) dm^3

gives $\qquad c=\frac{0.100\ mol}{2.00\ dm^3}=0.0500\ mol\ dm^{-3}$

b $\qquad c=\frac{n}{V}=\frac{0.0100\ mol}{1.00\ dm^3}=0.100\ mol\ dm^{-3}$

c $\qquad c=\frac{n}{V}=\frac{0.100\ mol}{0.500\ dm^3}=0.200\ mol\ dm^{-3}$

d $\qquad c=\frac{n}{V}=\frac{0.100\ mol}{0.250\ dm^3}=0.400\ mol\ dm^{-3}$

e $\qquad c=\frac{n}{V}=\frac{0.100\ mol}{0.100\ dm^3}=1.00\ mol\ dm^{-3}$

EXERCISE 24 **a** Substituting into the expression

$$n = \frac{m}{M}$$

where m = 8.50 g and M = 169.9 g mol^{-1}

gives

$$n = \frac{8.50 \text{ g}}{169.9 \text{ g mol}^{-1}} = 0.0500 \text{ mol}$$

Substituting into the expression

$$c = \frac{n}{V}$$

where n = 0.0500 mol and V = 1.00 dm^3

gives

$$c = \frac{0.0500 \text{ mol}}{1.00 \text{ dm}^3} = 0.0500 \text{ mol dm}^{-3}$$

Or, substituting $n = \frac{m}{M}$ into $c = \frac{n}{V}$

$$c = \frac{m}{MV} = \frac{8.50 \text{ g}}{169.9 \text{ g mol}^{-1} \times 1.00 \text{ dm}^3} = 0.0500 \text{ mol dm}^{-3}$$

b $$c = \frac{m}{MV} = \frac{10.7 \text{ g}}{214.0 \text{ g mol}^{-1} \times 0.250 \text{ dm}^3} = 0.200 \text{ mol dm}^{-3}$$

c $$c = \frac{m}{MV} = \frac{11.2 \text{ g}}{331.2 \text{ g mol}^{-1} \times 0.050 \text{ dm}^3} = 0.676 \text{ mol dm}^{-3}$$

d $$c = \frac{m}{MV} = \frac{14.3 \text{ g}}{294.1 \text{ g mol}^{-1} \times 0.250 \text{ dm}^3} = 0.194 \text{ mol dm}^{-3}$$

e $$c = \frac{m}{MV} = \frac{11.9 \text{ g}}{249.6 \text{ g mol}^{-1} \times 0.500 \text{ dm}^3} = 0.0954 \text{ mol dm}^{-3}$$

EXPERIMENT 2
Specimen results
Results Table 3

Molar mass of potassium hydrogenphthalate, M	204.1 g mol^{-1}
Mass of bottle and contents before transfer, m_1	15.47 g
Mass of bottle and contents after transfer, m_2	10.20 g
Mass of potassium hydrogenphthalate, $m = (m_1 - m_2)$	5.27 g
Amount of potassium hydrogenphthalate, $n = m/M$	2.58×10^{-2} mol
Volume of solution, V	0.250 dm^3
Concentration of potassium hydrogenphthalate, $c = n/V$	0.103 mol dm^{-3}

EXPERIMENT 2
Questions

1. **a** The concentration would be lower than calculated. From the expression $c = n/V$, a decrease in amount will reduce the value of the concentration.
   b The concentration would be greater than calculated. From the expression $c = n/V$, insufficient water (i.e. a decrease in V) will increase the value of the concentration.

EXERCISE 25

a Substituting into the expression

$$c = \frac{n}{V} \quad \text{in the form } n = cV$$

where c = 5.00 mol dm^{-3} and V = 4.00 dm^3
gives n = 5.00 mol dm^{-3} × 4.00 dm^3 = 20.0 mol
b $n = cV$ = 2.50 mol dm^{-3} × 1.00 dm^3 = 2.50 mol
c $n = cV$ = 0.439 mol dm^{-3} × 0.020 dm^3 = 8.78 × 10^{-3} mol

EXERCISE 26

a Substituting into the expression

$$c = \frac{n}{V} \quad \text{in the form } n = cV$$

where c = 0.0100 mol dm^{-3} and V = 1.00 dm^3
gives n = 0.100 mol dm^{-3} × 1.00 dm^3 = 0.100 mol
Substituting into the expression

$$n = \frac{m}{M} \quad \text{in the form } m = nM$$

where n = 0.100 mol and M = 58.4 g mol^{-1}
gives m = 0.100 mol × 58.4 g mol^{-1} = 5.84 g

Or, combining $c = \dfrac{n}{V}$ with $n = \dfrac{m}{M}$ and substituting

$m = nM = cVM$ = 0.100 mol dm^{-3} × 1.00 dm^3 × 58.4 g mol^{-1} = 5.84 g
b $m = cVM$ = 1.00 mol dm^{-3} × 0.500 dm^3 × 110.9 g mol^{-1} = 55.5 g
c $m = cVM$ = 0.200 mol dm^{-3} × 0.250 dm^3 × 158.0 g mol^{-1} = 7.90 g
d $m = cVM$ = 0.117 mol dm^{-3} × 0.200 dm^3 × 40.0 g mol^{-1} = 0.936 g

EXERCISE 27

a $$Ba(OH)_2 \text{ (aq)} + 2HCl \text{ (aq)} \rightarrow BaCl_2 \text{ (aq)} + 2H_2O \text{ (l)}$$

Let A refer to HCl and B to Ba(OH)$_2$. Substituting into the expression

$$\frac{c_A V_A}{c_B V_B} = \frac{a}{b}$$

where c_A = 0.0600 mol dm^{-3} $\qquad$ c_B = ?
$\qquad$ V_A = 25.0 cm^3 $\qquad\qquad$ V_B = 20.0 cm^3
$\qquad$ a = 2 $\qquad\qquad\qquad$ b = 1

gives $$\frac{0.0600 \text{ mol dm}^{-3} \times 25.0 \text{ cm}^3}{c_B \times 20.0 \text{ cm}^3} = \frac{2}{1}$$

Solving for c_B gives

$$c_B = \frac{0.0600 \text{ mol dm}^{-3} \times 25.0 \text{ cm}^3}{2 \times 20.0 \text{ cm}^3} = 0.0375 \text{ mol dm}^{-3}$$

b It is not necessary to convert from cm^3 to dm^3 because the units of volume cancel in the final expression.

EXERCISE 28 a
$$NaOH \text{ (aq)} + HNO_3 \text{ (aq)} \rightarrow NaNO_3 \text{ (aq)} + H_2O \text{ (l)}$$

Let A refer to $NaOH$ and B to HNO_3.
Substituting into the expression

$$\frac{c_A V_A}{c_B V_B} = \frac{a}{b}$$

where $c_A = 0.500 \text{ mol dm}^{-3}$ $c_B = 0.100 \text{ mol dm}^{-3}$
$V_A = ?$ $V_B = 50.0 \text{ cm}^3$

gives
$$\frac{0.500 \text{ mol dm}^{-3} \times V_A}{0.100 \text{ mol dm}^{-3} \times 50.0 \text{ cm}^3} = \frac{1}{1}$$

$$\therefore V_A = \frac{0.100 \text{ mol dm}^{-3} \times 50.0 \text{ cm}^3}{0.500 \text{ mol dm}^{-3}} = 10.0 \text{ cm}^3$$

b
$$\frac{c_A V_A}{c_B V_B} = \frac{a}{b} \quad \text{(A refers to NaOH, B to } H_2SO_4\text{)}$$

$$\therefore \frac{0.500 \text{ mol dm}^{-3} \times V_A}{0.262 \text{ mol dm}^{-3} \times 22.5 \text{ cm}^3} = \frac{2}{1}$$

and
$$V_A = \frac{2 \times 0.262 \times 22.5 \text{ cm}^3}{0.500} = 23.6 \text{ cm}^3$$

EXERCISE 29 Substituting into the expression:

$$\frac{c_A V_A}{c_B V_B} = \frac{a}{b}$$

where $c_A = 0.50 \text{ mol dm}^{-3}$ $c_B = 0.20 \text{ mol dm}^{-3}$
$V_A = 25.0 \text{ cm}^3$ $V_B = 31.3 \text{ cm}^3$

$$\frac{a}{b} = \frac{0.50 \text{ mol dm}^{-3} \times 25.0 \text{ cm}^3}{0.20 \text{ mol dm}^{-3} \times 31.3 \text{ cm}^3} = \frac{2}{1}$$

$\therefore a = 2, b = 1$.

EXPERIMENT 3

Specimen results

Results Table 4

Pipette solution	potassium hydrogenphthalate			0.0103	mol dm^{-3}	25.0 cm^3
Burette solution	sodium hydroxide			?	mol dm^{-3}	
Indicator	phenolphthalein					
		Trial	1	2	3	(4)
Burette readings	Final	26.9	26.80	27.45	26.15	—
	Initial	0.7	0.90	1.50	0.30	—
Volume used (titre)/cm^3		26.2	25.90	25.95	25.85	—
Mean titre/cm^3		25.9(0)				

Calculation

Let A refer to potassium hydrogenphthalate and B to sodium hydroxide.
1. Substituting into the expression

$$\frac{c_A V_A}{c_B V_B} = \frac{a}{b}$$

where $c_A = 0.103$ mol dm^{-3} $c_B = ?$
         $V_A = 25.0$ cm^3 $V_B = 25.9$ cm^3
         $a = 1$ $b = 1$

gives

$$\frac{0.103 \text{ mol dm}^{-3} \times 25.0 \text{ cm}^3}{c_B \times 25.9 \text{ cm}^3} = \frac{1}{1}$$

$$\therefore c_B = \frac{0.103 \text{ mol dm}^{-3} \times 25.0 \text{ cm}^3}{25.9 \text{ cm}^3} = 0.0994 \text{ mol dm}^{-3}$$

EXPERIMENT 3

Questions

1. **a** If the burette is dry (and clean), no effect. If the burette is wet, this will slightly dilute the NaOH so that slightly more of it is required. If V_B is increased, c_B will be **smaller** than it should be.
   b If the pipette is dry (and clean), no effect. If the pipette is wet, this will slightly dilute the acid so that slightly less NaOH is required. If V_B is decreased, c_B will be **greater** than it should be.
   c The recorded volume of NaOH will be greater than it should be, because it will include a bubble of air. If V_B is increased, c_B will be **smaller** than it should be.
   d No effect. The dilution occurs **after** the amount has been measured.
2. It is easier for the eye to detect the approach of the end-point when colour appears rather than when it disappears.
3. Sodium hydroxide solution attacks glass to some extent, especially the ground surfaces in some burette taps. Also, it absorbs carbon dioxide from the air, forming a crust of sodium carbonate. Both these actions can cause burette taps to seize up.

EXPERIMENT 4

Specimen results

Results Table 5

Pipette solution	iodine			0.0497	mol dm^{-3}	10.0 cm^3
Burette solution	sodium thiosulphate			0.0512	mol dm^{-3}	
Indicator	starch					
		Trial	1	2	3	(4)
Burette readings	Final	20.3	40.40	20.15	40.25	—
	Initial	0.0	20.30	0.10	20.15	—
Volume used (titre)/cm^3		20.3	20.10	20.05	20.10	—
Mean titre/cm^3		20.1(0)				

Calculation   1. Substituting into the expression

$$\frac{c_A V_A}{c_B V_B} = \frac{a}{b}$$ ('A' refers to $Na_2S_2O_3$, 'B' to I_2)

where $c_A = 0.0512$ mol dm^{-3} $c_B = 0.0497$ mol dm^{-3}
$V_A = 20.1$ cm^3 $V_B = 10.0$ cm^3
$a = ?$ $b = ?$

gives $\dfrac{a}{b} = \dfrac{0.0512 \text{ mol dm}^{-3} \times 20.1 \text{ cm}^3}{0.0497 \text{ mol dm}^{-3} \times 10.0 \text{ cm}^3} = \dfrac{2.07}{1}$

∴ $a = 2$ and $b = 1$.
So we can write for the equation:

$$2Na_2S_2O_3 \text{ (aq)} + I_2 \text{ (aq)} \rightarrow \text{Products}$$

2. The formula for the other compound is $Na_2S_4O_6$ (sodium tetrathionate).

$$2Na_2S_2O_3 \text{ (aq)} + I_2 \text{ (aq)} \rightarrow NaI \text{ (aq)} + ?$$

To balance I atoms, the stoichiometric coefficient of NaI must be 2.

$$2Na_2S_2O_3 \text{ (aq)} + I_2 \text{ (aq)} \rightarrow 2NaI + ?$$

The atoms unaccounted for are two of sodium, four of sulphur and six of oxygen, $Na_2S_4O_6$.
The balanced equation is

$$2Na_2S_2O_3 \text{ (aq)} + I_2 \text{ (aq)} \rightarrow 2NaI \text{ (aq)} + Na_2S_4O_6 \text{ (aq)}$$

(The empirical formula is NaS_2O_3, but $Na_2S_4O_6$ is preferred because it contains $S_4O_6^{2-}$ ions.)

EXPERIMENT 5

Specimen results

Results Table 6

Mass of bottle and contents before transfer, m_1	11.79 g
Mass of bottle and contents after transfer, m_2	10.21 g
Mass of sample, $m = (m_1 - m_2)$	1.58 g
Mass of $BaCl_2 \cdot xH_2O$ in 10.0 cm^3 of solution	0.0632 g

Results Table 7

Pipette solution	barium chloride			? mol dm^{-3}	10.0 cm^3		
Burette solution	silver nitrate			0.0506 mol dm^{-3}			
Indicator	starch						
		Trial	1	2	3	(4)
Burette readings	Final	10.4	20.65	30.90	41.10	—
	Initial	0.0	10.40	20.75	30.90	—
Volume used (titre)/cm^3		10.4	10.25	10.15	10.20	—
Mean titre/cm^3		10.2 (0)				

Calculation There is more than one way of tackling this problem. Here is one suggestion.

First calculate the masses of $BaCl_2$ and H_2O in each sample. The mass of $BaCl_2$ can be calculated indirectly from titration data and the mass of H_2O by difference. Next convert masses to relative amounts to determine x. We explain this step by step.

1. Amount of Cl in sample (as Cl^-)

$$Ag^+ (aq) + Cl^- (aq) \rightarrow AgCl (s)$$

$$\therefore \text{ amount of Cl} = \text{amount of } AgNO_3$$

$$= cV = 0.506 \text{ mol dm}^{-3} \times 0.0102 \text{ dm}^3$$

$$= 5.16 \times 10^{-4} \text{ mol}$$

2. Amount and mass of $BaCl_2$

$$BaCl_2 (s) + aq \rightarrow Ba^{2+} (aq) + 2Cl^- (aq)$$

$$\therefore \text{ amount of } BaCl_2 = \tfrac{1}{2} \times \text{amount of } Cl^-$$

$$= \tfrac{1}{2} \times 5.16 \times 10^{-4} \text{ mol} = 2.58 \times 10^{-4} \text{ mol}$$

$$\text{mass of } BaCl_2 = nM = 2.58 \times 10^{-4} \text{ mol} \times 208 \text{ g mol}^{-1}$$

$$= 0.0537 \text{ g}$$

3. Mass and amount of H_2O

$$\text{mass of } H_2O = \text{mass of } BaCl_2 \cdot xH_2O - \text{mass of } BaCl_2$$

$$= 0.0632 \text{ g} - 0.0537 \text{ g} = 0.0095 \text{ g}$$

$$\text{amount of } H_2O = \frac{m}{M} = \frac{0.0095 \text{ g}}{18.0 \text{ g mol}^{-1}} = 5.3 \times 10^{-4} \text{ mol}$$

4. Relative amounts

	$BaCl_2$	H_2O
Amount/mol	2.58×10^{-4}	5.3×10^{-4}
Amount/ smallest amount = relative amount	$\dfrac{2.58 \times 10^{-4}}{2.58 \times 10^{-4}} = 1.00$	$\dfrac{5.3 \times 10^{-4}}{2.58 \times 10^{-4}} = 2.1$

The relative amounts are very close to the integers 1 and 2.
$\therefore x = 2$ and the formula is $BaCl_2 \cdot 2H_2O$.

EXERCISE 30 First calculate the mass of Mg^{2+}, Cl^- and H_2O in the 0.203 g sample. The mass of Cl^- can be calculated from the titration data, the mass of H_2O from the percentage lost on dehydration and finally the mass of Mg^{2+} by difference.

Next, convert masses to relative amounts to give values for m and n.

The procedure can be summarised in a flow-chart, as follows:

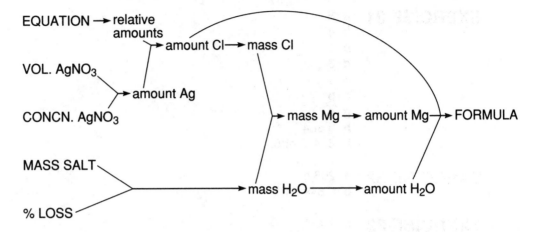

The detailed calculation follows, step by step.

1. Amount and mass of Cl

$$Ag^+ (aq) + Cl^- (aq) \rightarrow AgCl (s)$$

$$\therefore \text{ amount of Cl = amount of } AgNO_3$$
$$= cV = 0.100 \text{ mol dm}^{-3} \times 0.0200 \text{ dm}^3$$
$$= 2.00 \times 10^{-3} \text{ mol}$$
$$\therefore \text{ mass of Cl} = nM = 2.00 \times 10^{-3} \text{ mol} \times 35.5 \text{ g mol}^{-1} = 0.0710 \text{ g}$$

2. Mass and amount of H_2O

$$\text{mass of } H_2O = \text{loss in mass of sample}$$

$$= \frac{53.2}{100} \times 0.203 \text{ g} = 0.108 \text{ g}$$

$$\therefore \text{ amount of } H_2O = \frac{m}{M} = \frac{0.108 \text{ g}}{18.0 \text{ g mol}^{-1}} = 6.00 \times 10^{-3} \text{ mol}$$

3. Mass and amount of Mg

$$\text{mass of Mg = mass of salt} - \text{mass of Cl} - \text{mass of } H_2O$$

$$= 0.203 \text{ g} - 0.071 \text{ g} - 0.108 \text{ g} = 0.024 \text{ g}$$

$$\therefore \text{ amount of Mg} = \frac{m}{M} = \frac{0.024 \text{ g}}{24.0 \text{ g mol}^{-1}} = 1.00 \times 10^{-3} \text{ mol}$$

4. Relative amounts

	Mg	Cl	H_2O
Amount/mol	1.0×10^{-3}	2.0×10^{-3}	6.0×10^{-3}
Amount/ smallest amount = relative amount	$\frac{1.0}{1.0} = 1.0$	$\frac{2.0}{1.0} = 2.0$	$\frac{6.0}{1.0} = 6.0$

$\therefore m = 2$, $n = 6$ and the formula is $MgCl_2 \cdot 6H_2O$.

EXERCISE 31 **a** 3
b 4
c 2
d 3
e 3
f 5
g 4
h 3 or 4
i 3, 4, 5 or 6.

EXERCISE 32 **a** 208 g
b 0.649 dm^3.

EXERCISE 33 **a** 3.4 m
b 76 cm^3.

EXERCISE 34 **a** 3.0×10^{-3} mol
b 67.8 g.

EXERCISE 35 **a** 0.48 mol
b 2 g cm^{-3}.

■ Answers for unit – Atomic Structure

(Answers to questions from examination papers are provided by ILPAC and not by the examination boards.)

EXERCISE 36   The scale factor is given by:

$$\frac{\text{diameter of earth}}{\text{diameter of football}} = \frac{13000 \times 10^3 \text{ m}}{22 \times 10^{-2} \text{ m}} = 5.9 \times 10^7$$

∴ the diameter of an atom would become $5.9 \times 10^7 \times 0.32$ nm
$= 1.9 \times 10^7$ nm = 1.9 cm.
This is the diameter of a 1p piece. Correct answer = **b**

EXERCISE 37

$$\frac{\text{radius of atom}}{\text{radius of nucleus}} = \frac{10^{-10} \text{ m}}{10^{-15} \text{ m}} = 10^5$$

∴ if the nucleus were 1 mm in diameter, the atom would be 1×10^5 mm in diameter or 100 m.
This is approximately the length of a football pitch.

EXERCISE 38   The atomic number of an atom is the number of protons in its nucleus.
   The mass number of an atom is the total number of protons and neutrons in its nucleus. (Protons and neutrons are known collectively as nucleons.)

EXERCISE 39   Isotopes are atoms of the same element with different numbers of neutrons; e.g. nitrogen has two stable isotopes, one containing 7 protons and 7 neutrons, the other 7 protons and 8 neutrons.

EXERCISE 40   **a** W – 18;
   X – 19;
   Y – 19;
   Z – 18.
   In each case, the number of neutrons is subtracted from the mass number.
   b Isotopes: W and Z; X and Y.

EXERCISE 41   **a** i) $^{36}_{18}\text{Ar}$, $^{38}_{18}\text{Ar}$, $^{40}_{18}\text{Ar}$.
   ii) $^{63}_{29}\text{Cu}$, $^{65}_{29}\text{Cu}$.
   iii) $^{28}_{14}\text{Si}$, $^{29}_{14}\text{Si}$, $^{30}_{14}\text{Si}$.
   b $^{36}_{18}\text{Ar} - 18$, $^{38}_{18}\text{Ar} - 20$, $^{40}_{18}\text{Ar} - 22$.
   $^{63}_{29}\text{Cu} - 34$, $^{65}_{29}\text{Cu} - 36$.
   $^{28}_{14}\text{Si} - 14$, $^{29}_{14}\text{Si} - 15$, $^{30}_{14}\text{Si} - 16$.
   In each case, the subscript (atomic number) is subtracted from the superscript (mass number).

EXERCISE 42   **b** A vaporised sample   D   connection to vacuum pump
        B electron source   E   magnetic field
        C electric field   F   detector for positive ions

c **Vaporised sample** Atoms must be in the gaseous state before they can be ionised.

Electron source A stream of electrons is used to bombard the atoms of the vaporised sample and strip electrons off them, forming positive ions. The main process that takes place is, for an element X:

$$X\,(g) \rightarrow X^+\,(g) + e^-$$

The source is usually a tungsten filament which gives off electrons when a current is passed through it.

Electric field An electrode with a negative potential attracts the positive ions and accelerates them as they move towards it.

The electrode contains a pair of slits which further restricts the stream of ions to a very narrow beam.

Connection to a vacuum pump The whole apparatus is evacuated at the start of the experiment. This allows the positive ions to travel in straight lines without collision.

Magnetic field A powerful magnet sets up a magnetic field which deflects the positive ions in the beam. The extent of deflection depends on the mass and charge of the ion.

By altering the strength of the magnetic field, ions of different mass-to-charge ratio can be brought into focus on the detector.

Detector This is an electronic measuring device. The signal from the positive ions is amplified and recorded by a pen recorder giving a series of peaks corresponding to the different ions produced from the sample. In a mass spectrograph, the ions strike a photographic plate, producing a series of lines called a mass spectrum. In both cases, samples of known standards are also run and the unknowns worked out by comparison.

EXERCISE 43 a i) $^{222}_{86}Rn^+$, $^{220}_{86}Rn^+$.
ii) $^{220}_{86}Rn^+$.

Lighter isotopes are deflected more in a given magnetic field.
b i) Increase the strength of the magnetic field. This increases the deflection of the ions and would draw those at Y towards the detector.
ii) Decrease the strength of the electric field, by decreasing the voltage between the accelerator plates. This decreases the momentum of the ions and therefore increases their deflection in the magnetic field.
c Rn^{2+} ions would be deflected more than the ions at X and Y. For a given electric and magnetic field strength, the deflection of the ions depends on their mass-to-charge ratio. The smaller the ratio, the greater is the deflection.

EXERCISE 44 a $^{87}_{37}Rb$, $^{85}_{37}Rb$.
b The height of each peak is proportional to the relative abundance of the isotope it represents. In this case, $^{85}_{37}Rb$ is more than twice as abundant as $^{87}_{37}Rb$.

EXERCISE 45 **a** Height of lithium-6 peak = 0.50 cm
Height of lithium-7 peak = 6.30 cm
Substituting into the expression:

$$\% \text{ abundance} = \frac{\text{amount of isotope}}{\text{total amount of all isotopes}} \times 100$$

$$\% \text{ abundance of } ^6\text{Li} = \frac{0.50}{6.30 + 0.50} \times 100 = 7.4\%$$

$$\% \text{ abundance of } ^7\text{Li} = \frac{6.30}{6.30 + 0.50} \times 100 = 92.6\%$$

b Total mass of a hundred atoms = $(6 \times 7.4) + (7 \times 92.6)$ amu
$= 44.4 + 648.2$ amu $= 692.6$ amu
$= 693$ amu (3 significant figures)

Substituting into the expression:

$$\text{average mass} = \frac{\text{total mass}}{\text{number of atoms}}$$

$$\text{average mass} = \frac{693}{100} \text{ amu} = 6.93 \text{ amu}$$

$$\therefore \text{ relative atomic mass} = 6.93$$

EXERCISE 46 The mass/charge ratios refer to the singly-charged ions from the isotopes present in the sample: $^{20}_{10}\text{Ne}$, $^{21}_{10}\text{Ne}$, $^{22}_{10}\text{Ne}$.

The relative intensities show the relative abundance of each isotope in the sample. Substituting into the expression:

$$\% \text{ abundance} = \frac{\text{amount of isotope}}{\text{total amount of all isotopes}} \times 100$$

$$\% \text{ abundance of } ^{20}\text{Ne} = \frac{0.910}{0.910 + 0.0026 + 0.088} \times 100 = 91\%$$

$$\% \text{ abundance of } ^{21}\text{Ne} = \frac{0.0026}{0.910 + 0.0026 + 0.088} \times 100 = 0.26\%$$

$$\% \text{ abundance of } ^{22}\text{Ne} = \frac{0.088}{0.910 + 0.0026 + 0.088} \times 100 = 8.8\%$$

(Did you notice that the sum of the relative intensities is 1?)

Total mass of 100 atoms = $(20 \times 91) + (21 \times 0.26) + (22 \times 8.8)$
$= 1820 + 5.46 + 193.6 = 2.02 \times 10^3$ amu

$$\text{Average mass} = \frac{\text{total mass}}{\text{number of atoms}} = \frac{2.02 \times 10^3 \text{ amu}}{100} = 20.2 \text{ amu}$$

$$\therefore \text{ relative atomic mass} = 20.2$$

EXERCISE 47   **a** $^{50}_{24}$Cr – 4.31%; $^{52}_{24}$Cr – 83.76%; $^{53}_{24}$Cr – 9.55%; $^{54}_{24}$Cr – 2.38%.
b–d

Figure 46

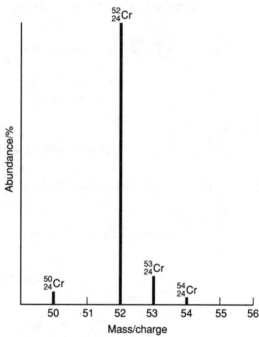

Total mass of 100 atoms $= (50 \times 4.31) + (52 \times 83.76)$

$$+ (53 \times 9.55) + (54 \times 2.38)$$

$$= 215.5 + 4355.2 + 506.15 + 128.52$$

$$= 5.21 \times 10^3 \text{ amu}$$

$$\therefore \text{ average mass } = \frac{5.21 \times 10^3 \text{ amu}}{100} = 52.1 \text{ amu}$$

and relative atomic mass $= 52.1$

EXERCISE 48   **a** i) The positions of Te and I would be reversed.
ii) The positions of Ar and K would be reversed.
b There is only one stable isotope of iodine – $^{127}_{53}$I. The relative atomic mass is therefore 127. Tellurium has no fewer than eight stable isotopes, but the most abundant are $^{128}_{52}$Te and $^{130}_{52}$Te, each of which has more neutrons than $^{127}_{53}$I, but fewer protons. Thus, the relative atomic mass of tellurium is greater than that of iodine, even though the atomic number is smaller. In the same way, heavy isotopes of argon, mainly $^{40}_{18}$Ar, give it a greater relative atomic mass than potassium, which consists mainly of $^{39}_{19}$K.

EXERCISE 49

Mass/charge ratio	Species
35	$^{35}_{17}$Cl$^+$
37	$^{37}_{17}$Cl$^+$
70	$(^{35}_{17}$Cl—$^{35}_{17}$Cl$)^+$
72	$(^{35}_{17}$Cl—$^{37}_{17}$Cl$)^+$
74	$(^{37}_{17}$Cl—$^{37}_{17}$Cl$)^+$

EXERCISE 50   **a** P – α particles ($^4_2$He); Q – γ rays; R – β particles ($^0_1$e).
b A magnetic field operating in a direction perpendicular to the plane of the paper would cause a similar pattern of deflection.

EXERCISE 51

Table 5

Emission	Nature	Relative mass and charge		Symbol	Extent of deflection in electric or magnetic field	Relative penetration
Alpha, α	Helium nuclei	4	+2	$^{4}_{2}He$	small	1
Beta, β	electrons	$\frac{1}{1840}$	−1	$^{0}_{-1}e$	large	100
Gamma, γ	electro-magnetic radiation	none	none	none	none	10000

EXERCISE 52

$^{1}_{0}n \rightarrow\, ^{1}_{1}H +\, ^{0}_{-1}e$

EXERCISE 53

a $^{212}_{84}Po \rightarrow\, ^{4}_{2}He +\, ^{208}_{82}Pb$

b $^{220}_{86}Rn \rightarrow\, ^{4}_{2}He +\, ^{216}_{84}Po$

EXERCISE 54

a $^{212}_{84}Po \rightarrow\, ^{0}_{-1}e +\, ^{212}_{85}At$

b $^{24}_{11}Na \rightarrow\, ^{0}_{-1}e +\, ^{24}_{12}Mg$

c $^{108}_{47}Ag \rightarrow\, ^{0}_{-1}e +\, ^{108}_{48}Cd$

EXERCISE 55

a $^{226}_{88}Ra \rightarrow\, ^{4}_{2}He +\, ^{222}_{86}Rn$

b $^{43}_{19}K \rightarrow\, ^{0}_{-1}e +\, ^{43}_{20}Ca$

c $^{43}_{20}Ca \rightarrow\, ^{4}_{2}He +\, ^{39}_{18}Ar$

EXERCISE 56

a For α emission, the atomic number decreases by two and the mass number decreases by four.

b For β emission, the atomic number increases by one and the mass number remains the same.

EXERCISE 57

a The half-life of a radioactive isotope is the time taken for a given amount of isotope to decay to half the original amount.

b Since radioactive decay is an exponential process, it carries on to infinity, or at least to levels where the rate is no longer statistically significant. In other words, decay becomes slower and slower but never actually stops. This means that it is impossible to measure the 'total life' of a radioisotope.

EXERCISE 58 a
Figure 47

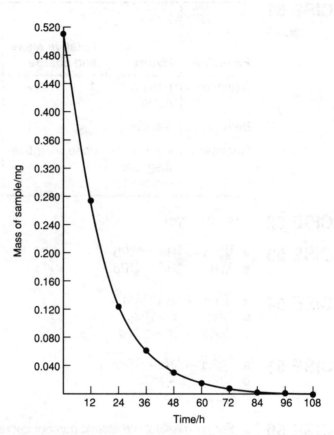

b The rate decreases as the reaction proceeds. Since the rate of decay is proportional to the amount of isotope remaining at any time, it decreases exponentially as the amount of radioisotope decreases.

c Theoretically, the amount would never reach zero, as this is an exponential process.

d The shape of the curve would be the same if activity had been plotted because activity is proportional to mass.

e There are two ways of answering this question.

i) The graph shows the mass of the sample decreasing by half every 12 hours, i.e. the half-life is 12 hours and 10 half-lives = 120 hours.

Since activity is proportional to mass, the percentage of activity remaining after 10 half lives

$$= \frac{\text{mass after 120 hours}}{\text{original mass}} = 100$$

$$= \frac{0.0005 \text{ mg}}{0.512 \text{ mg}} \times 100 = 0.1\%$$

ii) Without reference to the graph, an answer is obtained more precisely: fraction left after 10 half-lives

$$= \tfrac{1}{2} \times \tfrac{1}{2} \times \tfrac{1}{2} \times \tfrac{1}{2} \times \tfrac{1}{2} \times \tfrac{1}{2} \times \tfrac{1}{2} \times \tfrac{1}{2} \times \tfrac{1}{2} \times \tfrac{1}{2}$$

$$(\tfrac{1}{2})^{10} = 9.77 \times 10^{-4}$$

$$\% = \text{fraction} \times 100 = 0.0977\%$$

EXERCISE 59
  a $^{14}_{7}N + ^{1}_{0}n \rightarrow ^{14}_{6}C + ^{1}_{1}H$.

  b The relative activity of the sample compared with the activity of new wood

$$= \frac{\text{activity of sample}}{\text{activity of new wood}} = \frac{7.5 \text{ counts min}^{-1} \text{ g}^{-1}}{15 \text{ counts min}^{-1} \text{ g}^{-1}} = 0.50$$

Since the sample has an activity of half that of new wood, one half-life has elapsed.

$$\therefore \text{ year in which tomb was built} = 1982 \text{ AD} - 5730 = 3748 \text{ BC}$$

The method is not as accurate as this answer implies. It would be safer to say the tomb was built between 3700 BC and 3800 BC.

  c The amount of carbon-14 in the atmosphere is assumed to be constant so that the percentage of carbon-14 in freshly-grown wood is also constant.

EXERCISE 60
  a First ionisation energy is the energy required to remove each outermost electron from one mole of atoms of an element in its gaseous state.

  b $Na (g) \rightarrow Na^{+} (g) + e^{-}$

  c First ionisation energy of sodium = 500 kJ mol^{-1}.

EXERCISE 61
  a $Al (g) \rightarrow Al^{+} (g) + e^{-}$
      $Al^{+} (g) \rightarrow Al^{2+} (g) + e^{-}$
      $Al^{2+} (g) \rightarrow Al^{3+} (g) + e^{-}$

  b The values of the ionisation energies increase in the order 1st < 2nd < 3rd.

  c Extra energy is needed to overcome the attractive forces between the leaving electrons and ions of increasing positive charge.

EXERCISE 62
  a

Figure 48

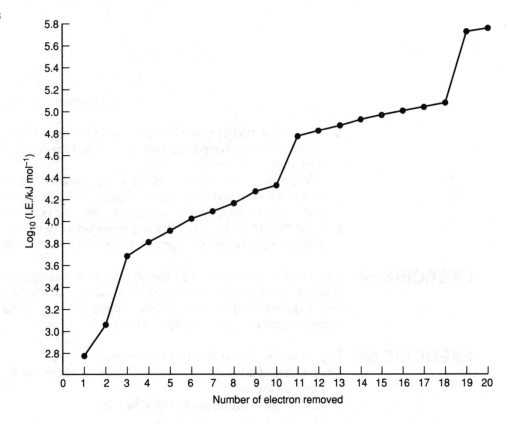

b The discontinuities in the graph indicate that there are two electrons in the outermost shell (with highest energy), eight electrons in each of the middle two shells and two electrons in the shell closest to the nucleus (with lowest energy).

c It would have been impossible to fit the non-logarithmic values all on a convenient scale. The first few values would be almost indistinguishable.

d The second electron is harder to remove than the first one as the attraction between the mono-positively charged ion and the outermost electrons has to be overcome. Successive electrons need increasing amounts of energy to remove them as the ion becomes increasingly positively charged.

EXERCISE 63   **a**

Figure 49

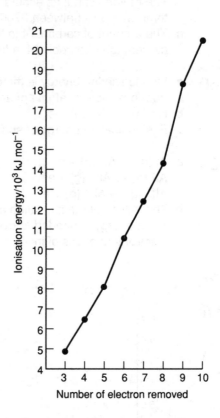

b The small jump between the eighth and ninth electrons indicates that the third electron shell is divided into two sub-shells, with two electrons at a lower energy level than the other six.

You may also see a slight discontinuity between the fifth and sixth electrons on your graph. The sixth electron is slightly more difficult to remove than extrapolation of the line suggests. We shall return to this idea later in the unit.

c In the third shell, the electrons are arranged in two sub-shells: two electrons, of lower energy, nearer the nucleus and six electrons, of higher energy, further from it.

EXERCISE 64   The orbital model is based on the probability of finding an electron in a given volume of space. It is not possible to state precisely where an electron will be at a given moment, only to define a region of space where there is a high probability that it will be located. Such a region of space is called an orbital.

EXERCISE 65   The second shell contains eight electrons.
The number of orbitals is n^2 and $n = 2$ for the second shell.
∴ there are four orbitals
∴ number of electrons per orbital = $^8/_4$ = 2.

EXERCISE 66 The subscripts *x*, *y* and *z* stand for the *x*, *y* and *z* axes and indicate the position the orbitals occupy in space relative to each other.

EXERCISE 67
a i) Two electrons.
   ii) Six electrons.
b i) Spherical.
   ii) Dumb-bell shaped.

EXERCISE 68

Table 9

Shell	No. and type of orbitals	Maximum number of electrons in each set of orbitals	Maximum number of electrons in the shell
First shell	one s	2	2
Second shell	one s	2	
	three p	6	8
Third shell	one s	2	
	three p	6	
	five d	10	18
Fourth shell	one s	2	
	three p	6	
	five d	10	
	seven f	14	32

EXERCISE 69 1s 2s 2p 3s 3p 4s 3d 4p 5s 4d

EXERCISE 70

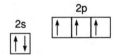

EXERCISE 71
   a $_5$B:
       b $_6$C:
       c $_7$N:

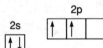

EXERCISE 72

   a $_6$C:
   b $_7$N:

EXERCISE 73

a (Ne)   3s [↑]

b (Ne)   3s [↑↓]

EXERCISE 74

a (Ne)$3s^2 3p^4$.
b (Ne)$3s^2 3p^5$.
c (Ne)$3s^2 3p^6$.

EXERCISE 75

a i) (He)$2s^2 2p^6$.
 ii) (He)$2s^2 2p^6$.
b Neon.

EXERCISE 76

a $1s^2 2s^2 2p^6 3s^2 3p^6 4s^1$ or (Ar)$4s^1$.
b $1s^2 2s^2 2p^6 3s^2 3p^6 4s^2$ or (Ar)$4s^2$.

EXERCISE 77

$1s^2 2s^2 2p^6 3s^2 3p^6 3d^1 4s^2$ or (Ar)$3d^1 4s^2$.

EXERCISE 78

a $_{22}$Ti i) [orbital diagram: 1s ↑↓ | 2s ↑↓ | 2p ↑↓ ↑↓ ↑↓ | 3s ↑↓ | 3p ↑↓ ↑↓ ↑↓ | 3d ↑ ↑ _ _ _ | 4s ↑↓]

ii) $1s^2 2s^2 2p^6 3s^2 3p^6 3d^2 4s^2$ or (Ar)$3d^2 4s^2$

b $_{23}$V i) [orbital diagram: 1s ↑↓ | 2s ↑↓ | 2p ↑↓ ↑↓ ↑↓ | 3s ↑↓ | 3p ↑↓ ↑↓ ↑↓ | 3d ↑ ↑ ↑ _ _ | 4s ↑↓]

ii) $1s^2 2s^2 2p^6 3s^2 3p^6 3d^3 4s^2$ or (Ar)$3d^3 4s^2$

c $_{26}$Fe i) [orbital diagram: 1s ↑↓ | 2s ↑↓ | 2p ↑↓ ↑↓ ↑↓ | 3s ↑↓ | 3p ↑↓ ↑↓ ↑↓ | 3d ↑↓ ↑ ↑ ↑ ↑ | 4s ↑↓]

ii) $1s^2 2s^2 2p^6 3s^2 3p^6 3d^6 4s^2$ or (Ar)$3d^6 4s^2$

EXERCISE 79

a $_{31}$Ga$^+$ i) [orbital diagram: 1s ↑↓ | 2s ↑↓ | 2p ↑↓ ↑↓ ↑↓ | 3s ↑↓ | 3p ↑↓ ↑↓ ↑↓ | 3d ↑↓ ↑↓ ↑↓ ↑↓ ↑↓ | 4s ↑↓]

ii) $1s^2 2s^2 2p^6 3s^2 3p^6 3d^{10} 4s^2$ or (Ar)$3d^{10} 4s^2$

b $_{33}$As i) [orbital diagram: 1s ↑↓ | 2s ↑↓ | 2p ↑↓ ↑↓ ↑↓ | 3s ↑↓ | 3p ↑↓ ↑↓ ↑↓ | 3d ↑↓ ↑↓ ↑↓ ↑↓ ↑↓ | 4s ↑↓ | 4p ↑ ↑ ↑]

ii) $1s^2 2s^2 2p^6 3s^2 3p^6 3d^{10} 4s^2 4p^3$ or (Ar)$3d^{10} 4s^2 4p^3$

c $_{35}$Br$^-$ i) [orbital diagram: 1s ↑↓ | 2s ↑↓ | 2p ↑↓ ↑↓ ↑↓ | 3s ↑↓ | 3p ↑↓ ↑↓ ↑↓ | 3d ↑↓ ↑↓ ↑↓ ↑↓ ↑↓ | 4s ↑↓ | 4p ↑↓ ↑↓ ↑↓]

ii) $1s^2 2s^2 2p^6 3s^2 3p^6 3d^{10} 4s^2 4p^6$ or (Kr)

EXERCISE 80   6s 4f 5d 6p

EXERCISE 81
a   The s-, p-, d- and f-blocks are named after the last sub-shells to be filled in the build-up (aufbau) of these elements.

b   No. The number of a period is the number of the quantum shell which **starts** to fill. However, the quantum shell is not completely **filled** by the end of periods 4, 5 and 6: For example, the third shell is not completed until the end of period 4. Summarising:

Period 4.   3d orbitals being filled in d-block elements
Period 5.   4d orbitals being filled in d-block elements
Period 6.   5d orbitals being filled in d-block elements
             4f orbitals being filled in f-block elements

EXERCISE 82   a

Figure 50

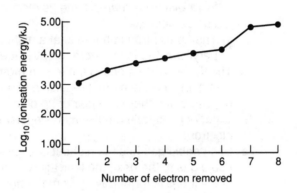

b $1s^2 2s^2 2p^4$.
c   Group VI.
d X^{2-}.

EXERCISE 83
a   X. (High first I.E. – no major 'jumps'.)
b   Y. (Jump from 1st to 2nd I.E.)
c   Z. (Jump from 2nd to 3rd I.E.)

EXERCISE 84

Figure 51

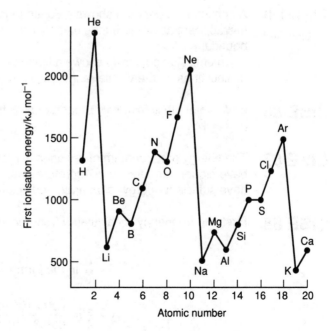

EXERCISE 85

a Helium has one more proton in the nucleus than hydrogen. This increases the force of attraction on the electrons, which are both in the same shell, and makes it more difficult to remove one.

b The outer electron in the lithium atom is in a shell (2s) which is unoccupied in a helium atom. Despite the increased nuclear charge, the outer electron is relatively easy to remove for two reasons:
   i) The inner electrons (1s) are interposed between the nucleus and the outer electrons, reducing the attractive force. This effect is known as 'shielding' or 'screening'.
   ii) The outer electron is further from the nucleus in lithium than in helium. This also contributes to reducing the attractive force, but the reason given in i) is more important.

c As in **b**, there are two reasons:
   i) The outer 2p electron in boron is more effectively shielded from the nucleus by inner electrons than are the 2s electrons in beryllium, despite the increased nuclear charge.
   ii) The 2p electron in boron is at a higher energy level than the 2s electrons in beryllium and is therefore, on average, further from the nucleus.

d The three 2p electrons in a nitrogen atom are unpaired, i.e. each 2p orbital is singly occupied, and the mutual repulsion of these electrons is not great. However, in an oxygen atom, there is a pair of 2p electrons, and since these two electrons experience mutual repulsion, it is easier to remove one of them than an unpaired electron.

e Each noble gas has the highest first ionisation energy in its period. Moving from one noble gas to the next, the ionisation energy decreases. In each case, the outer shell of electrons is further away from the nucleus and more effectively screened from it by the shells of lower energy. This decreases the effective nuclear charge and lowers the energy needed to remove an electron.

f The alkali metals have the lowest ionisation energy in their respective periods. The explanation of the decrease in ionisation energy in going from one alkali metal to the next is similar to that for the noble gases. In each case, the electron being removed is one shell further from the nucleus so that the effective nuclear charge is decreased and less energy is needed to remove the electron.

EXPERIMENT 6
Question

A continuous spectrum shows a continuous range of wavelengths. In the visible range, this appears as broad bands of colour merging into one another with no sharp boundaries.

An emission spectrum shows a limited number of wavelengths, which appear as distinct lines. In the visible range, the lines appear in different colours.

EXERCISE 86

a Wavelength is inversely proportional to frequency.
b $\lambda \propto 1/v$.

EXERCISE 87

The energy of a quantum of radiation is proportional to its frequency. Ultraviolet rays have higher frequency and, therefore, more energy than infrared rays. Ultraviolet rays have sufficient energy to damage body cells whereas infrared rays do not.

EXERCISE 88

First, the frequency is calculated from the wavelength by substituting into the equation:

$$\lambda = \frac{c}{v} \text{ in the form } v = \frac{c}{\lambda}$$

$$v = \frac{c}{\lambda} = \frac{3.00 \times 10^8 \text{ m s}^{-1}}{656.3 \times 10^{-9} \text{ m}} = 4.57 \times 10^{14} \text{ s}^{-1}$$

The energy is given by substituting into Planck's equation:

$$E = hv$$

$$\therefore E = 6.63 \times 10^{-34} \text{ J s} \times 4.57 \times 10^{14} \text{ s}^{-1} = 3.03 \times 10^{-19} \text{ J}$$

Alternatively, combining $\lambda = c/v$ with $E = hv$ and substituting

$$E = \frac{hc}{\lambda} = \frac{6.63 \times 10^{-34} \text{ J s} \times 3.00 \times 10^{8} \text{ m s}^{-1}}{656.3 \times 10^{-9} \text{ m}} = 3.03 \times 10^{-19} \text{ J}$$

EXERCISE 89

a The point where the spectral lines merge corresponds to electron transitions between $n = 2$ and $n = \infty$.

b If $n = \infty$, the electron has effectively left the atom.

c No. The energy value at this point is the energy required to remove an electron from the $n = 2$ level. Ionisation energy is the energy required to remove an electron from its ground state, in this case the $n = 1$ level.

EXERCISE 90

a The lines in each series get closer together at higher frequencies.

b In each series, the high frequency lines are caused by electron transitions from the highest energy levels.
   At high energies, the difference between energy levels gets smaller and smaller until they become indistinguishable.

EXERCISE 91

The Lyman series would be suitable for determining the ionisation energy of hydrogen as it includes radiation emitted from electron transitions from the highest energy levels to the ground state.

EXERCISE 92

a The convergence limit represents the point at which an electron has gained enough energy to leave the atom completely. At this point, ionisation has taken place. If the frequency of radiation corresponding to this point on the spectrum is known, the energy can be calculated using Planck's relationship, $E = hv$. This is the ionisation energy of the atom.

b The Balmer series is produced by electron transitions between higher energy levels and the $n = 2$ level; the Brackett series by transitions between higher levels and the $n = 4$ level. Neither series includes energy emitted during a transition from the highest level to the ground state. Unless appropriate adjustments are made, ionisation energies calculated using the convergence limits of these series would be too low.

EXERCISE 93

a Steel can be kept molten while awaiting analysis. This makes for faster production with no need for re-melting 'out of specification' castings, thus saving time and energy. Cost of analysis is also reduced.

b In a medical laboratory a flame photometer is routinely used to analyse for sodium and potassium. It is a much cheaper instrument than an atomic emission spectrometer and simpler to use.